BRAIN C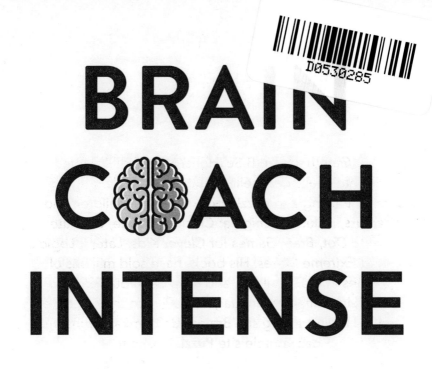ACH INTENSE

40-DAY
TRAINING
PROGRAMME

DR GARETH MOORE

Michael O'Mara Books Limited

First published in Great Britain in 2020 by
Michael O'Mara Books Limited
9 Lion Yard
Tremadoc Road
London SW4 7NQ

A CIP catalogue record for this book is available from the
British Library.

Papers used by Michael O'Mara Books Limited are natural,
recyclable products made from wood grown in sustainable
forests. The manufacturing processes conform to the
environmental regulations of the country of origin.

ISBN: 978-1-78929-239-8 in paperback print format

1 2 3 4 5 6 7 8 9 10

Designed and typeset by Gareth Moore

Printed and bound by CPI Group (UK) Ltd, Croydon, CR0 4YY

www.mombooks.com

CONTENTS

Introduction 7

Day 1   Simple Loop .8

Day 2   Dominoes 12

Day 3   King's Journey 16

Day 4   Mazes 20

Day 5   Sudoku 24

Day 6   Number Darts 28

Day 7   Shape Counting 32

Day 8   Fences 36

Day 9   No Four in a Row 40

Day 10 Hanjie 44

Day 11 Fillomino 48

Day 12 Tents 52

Day 13 Number Link 56

Day 14 Shikaku 60

Day 15 Yin Yang 64

Day 16 Hitori 68

Day 17 Kakuro 72

Day 18 Touchy 76

Day 19 Hashi / Bridges 80

Day 20 Snake 84

Day 21   Frame Sudoku. .88

Day 22   Minesweeper 92

Day 23   Spiral Galaxies 96

Day 24   Futoshiki. 100

Day 25   Easy as A, B, C 104

Day 26   Train Tracks. .108

Day 27   Arrow Sudoku. 112

Day 28   Battleships 116

Day 29   Akari / Light-up. 120

Day 30   Killer Sudoku. 124

Day 31   Star Battle. 128

Day 32   Thermo Sudoku 132

Day 33   Kropki. 136

Day 34   Heyawake. 140

Day 35   Calcudoku. 144

Day 36   Nurikabe. 148

Day 37   Yajilin 152

Day 38   Slitherlink 156

Day 39   Jigsaw Sudoku 160

Day 40   Skyscrapers. .164

          Solutions. 168

INTRODUCTION

Welcome to *Brain Coach Intense: 40 Day Training Programme*, packed from cover to cover with a hugely varied range of puzzles.

Each day a new type of puzzle is introduced, with the puzzles becoming progressively more complex to solve as the book continues, so it's best to start at the beginning and work through in day order.

An estimated solve time is given for every puzzle, but your own times may vary considerably depending on your previous experience. Nonetheless they provide an indication of the relative difficulties of the various puzzles, particularly within a given day.

Most days include two pages of 'Solving tutor' hints and tips, which give either general guidance or specific steps to get started on that page's puzzle. Work through them step by step in order to get the maximum benefit from each page.

The solving tips often refer to particular rows and columns. In each case it is assumed that row 1 is at the very top, and column 1 is on the very left.

Some puzzles take longer than others, so there is no need to complete all of a 'day' in a single calendar day – although you can certainly use the book in such a way if you wish.

Full solutions to the puzzles are given at the back of the book, if you need them. Good luck!

SIMPLE LOOP

+ Draw a loop which visits every white square

INSTRUCTIONS

Draw a single loop using only horizontal and vertical lines that visits every white square exactly once each. It cannot enter any shaded square. Because it can only visit each square once, this also means that it cannot cross over itself at any point.

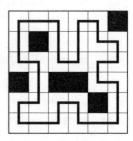

MENTAL PROCESSES

This is a beautifully simple puzzle with clean, straightforward rules – draw a loop – and a rewarding mix of observational and deductive reasoning required to solve. There are no complex rules to keep in mind, so you can concentrate immediately on the logic from the very first time you pick up your pencil. It's good practice for thinking about how to satisfy the more involved constraints of later puzzles.

Expert solving time
8 MINUTES

▶ SOLVING TUTOR ◀

PUZZLE 1

⧗ **1** MINUTE

▶ Start by looking at the corners. The loop has to visit every white square, so for the three unshaded corners there must be lines entering the corner square both horizontally and vertically from the two neighbouring squares.

▶ Since the lines must join to form a loop, any disconnected lines must be extended. Next up, extend the lines from the corners into squares they must go into, given the shading.

▶ There must be only one loop, not multiple loops, so also extend the loop in any directions necessary to prevent creating smaller loops that don't connect to the rest.

▶ As you solve, areas that become effectively 'new corners' – i.e. squares with only two possible connections – are created, so continue applying the same logic repeatedly.

▶ That's all that's required for this first puzzle.

PUZZLE 2

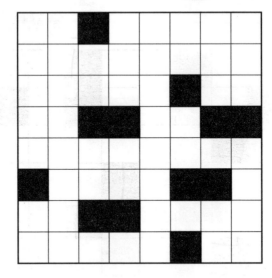

► Start by applying the deductions described on the previous page, and you'll end up with a situation where there are only eight or so squares that don't yet have any loop segments in.

► At this point you'll need to take a visual step back and look at the puzzle as more of a whole, rather than just locally at the individual line endings. Can you see how it must connect to form a single loop?

► As you progress, the placed parts of the loop will break the grid into separate unsolved areas. Bear in mind that every area must have an *even* number of line ends in it, so that they can all join together without leaving a line segment that doesn't pair up and join the rest of the loop. So if drawing a line in a particular direction would 'seal off' an odd number of line segments in one area of the grid then you know that that line must go another direction instead.

► TRY IT ◄

Now you're ready to try this more complex puzzle:

PUZZLE 3

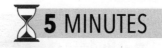

5 MINUTES

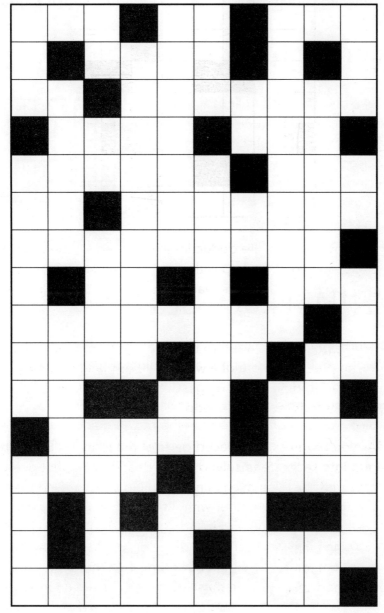

DOMINOES

+ Draw lines to place a full set of dominoes into the grid

INSTRUCTIONS

Draw along the dashed lines to divide the grid into 1×2 and 2×1 regions, so that all of the given set of dominoes is placed into the grid once each. A check-off chart is provided for keeping track of which dominoes have already been placed. In this puzzle, a '0' represents a blank on a traditional domino.

1	1	2	3	1	1
2	0	0	0	2	3
2	3	3	3	1	4
2	3	4	4	4	4
1	4	0	0	2	0

MENTAL PROCESSES

Dominoes puzzles typically don't require complex logic, but they do require careful observation. Initial placements are usually based on checking for unique number combinations, and a mistake made at this point will doom the entire puzzle. It's also useful to be able to scan the puzzle quickly, so you don't need to laboriously work through all possible dominoes one-by-one to find your next break-in.

Expert solving time
35 MINUTES

▶ SOLVING TUTOR ◀

PUZZLE 1 (0-4)

⏳ **5 MINUTES**

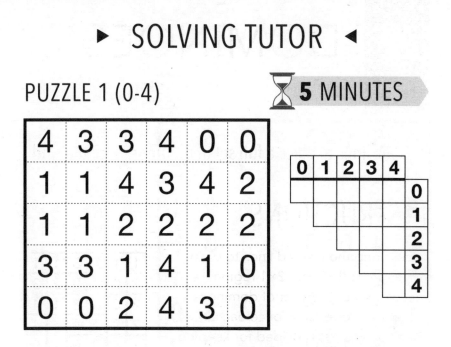

▶ This puzzle involves placing a set of 15 dominoes into the grid, corresponding to real-world dominoes with up to four dots on them. Start by looking for dominoes that appear in only one place. For example, in this puzzle there is only one place that the 1–0 domino can be drawn, so mark it in near the bottom right. Then cross it off on the chart too.

▶ Each time you draw in a domino, you limit the possible locations for other dominoes. For example, placing the 1–0 domino removes one of the three possible locations for the 0–0 domino.

▶ Check for when a domino is forced, since all squares are used. For example, after placing the 1–0 domino then the 3–0 domino beneath it is forced.

▶ Draw lines between other occurrences of an already-placed domino. For example, after the 3–0 is located at the bottom right then the touching 3 and 0 squares at the bottom left must be separated – which in turn forces the 0–0 domino.

PUZZLE 2 (0-6)

⏳ **10** MINUTES

5	5	0	2	2	4	5	5
0	2	4	4	6	4	1	0
3	3	6	3	4	6	2	1
0	4	6	3	0	1	3	5
5	2	1	2	6	3	1	1
1	2	6	0	0	4	3	6
5	6	1	0	5	4	3	2

0	1	2	3	4	5	6

- ▶ This puzzle involves the full normal set of dominoes, from 0 to 6, corresponding to zero (blank) up to six dots on a traditional domino. Other than the larger set, it works in exactly the same way as the smaller puzzle did.

- ▶ Solve in the same way as described previously, looking for unique dominoes and then placing what's forced in turn.

- ▶ Sometimes you know that a domino must use a certain square, but not its orientation (because a given digit touches on multiple sides). In this case, draw in the edges that you can be sure of, to help force adjacent dominoes.

- ▶ Remember that every remaining continuous area of the puzzle not yet assigned to dominoes must have an *even* number of squares in it, since no squares are left over and dominoes always cover two squares. Sometimes this allows you to draw lines in certain places, which can help a lot.

▶ TRY IT ◀

PUZZLE 3 (0-8)

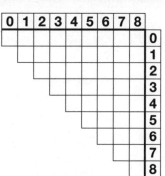 **20** MINUTES

4	8	3	0	4	7	6	6	1
7	8	5	8	5	1	0	5	6
5	6	5	4	8	4	0	5	2
4	1	2	5	2	8	7	7	3
1	3	3	8	3	4	6	7	3
6	4	6	0	5	7	8	3	8
1	1	7	2	2	0	1	7	5
0	2	2	6	3	6	3	0	0
1	8	1	3	4	2	0	1	8
4	4	0	7	7	2	6	5	2

Place dominoes from 0 to 8 in this trickier puzzle.

0	1	2	3	4	5	6	7	8	
									0
									1
									2
									3
									4
									5
									6
									7
									8

KING'S JOURNEY

+ Place numbers from 1 up to the number of squares
+ The numbers must form a path of increasing value

INSTRUCTIONS

Place a number from 1 to 16 (or the size of the grid as given) into each empty square, so that each number appears exactly once in the finished grid. Numbers must be placed so as to form a path from 1 to the highest value, moving to a square one higher in value at every

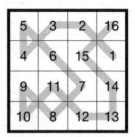

step. Steps must be as a king moves in chess – i.e. left, right, up, down or diagonally between adjacent squares.

MENTAL PROCESSES

King's journey puzzles often involve making sensible guesses, and then making small adjustments as the solve progresses to shift numbers into the exact squares they fit in. In this respect, they are a great example of a step-by-step optimization process, where an initial guess is slowly refined and perfected.

Expert solving time
35 MINUTES

PUZZLE 1  ## PUZZLE 2

			6
	5		
	1		
16			11

	2	28	26	25	24
1					23
5		36		30	
6			35		
	11				32
10		12		16	

Place 1–16 in puzzle 1, and place 1–36 in puzzle 2.

▶ The start and end of the path can be tricky to locate, but in the puzzles in this chapter they are always given. This means, therefore, that every other number must have a connection *in* to it and a connection *out* from it. The corners, and to a lesser extent the edges, are therefore much more constrained than the middle of the grid, so it's best to start here if possible.

▶ Look for numbers that are two apart. Can you place an in-between number straight away?

▶ Also look for numbers that are the maximum number of squares apart they possibly can be, such as numbers three apart in value that are three squares from one another. The path must travel directly from one to the other, although the further apart they are then the more possible routes there are. It may be worth marking in a guess at a route between them, making clear that these aren't final numbers, so that you can begin to make progress.

PUZZLE 3

5				42	45		52
	2		41		47		
1			61	60			
	8					55	
9	11		37		63		
						64	
25			13				
22			19		15		33

Place 1 to 64 in this puzzle.

► Remember that the path can cross itself diagonally. It's easy to think that you have made the puzzle impossible, when in fact there may be a perfectly straightforward way for the path to continue through a seeming dead end.

► As you start to fill the grid, look at the squares that remain empty. Is it actually still possible for a part of the path to pass through there, and if so will it also be connecting numbers as required? If not, it's time to adjust parts of the path you've already drawn in.

► If an area of the grid is causing trouble, leave it and tackle a completely different area – as the new placements eventually expand into the previous area, all may become clear.

▶ TRY IT ◀

PUZZLE 4

⏳ **18** MINUTES

85	86	87				78			98
			81	80		76			100
	54	55				74		1	
	50				43			95	
	49	47		58		42			4
65			61					7	
	63	62		69	70		18		
								17	
34		29	25	24			16		
					22			14	13

Place 1 to 100 in this puzzle.

MAZES

+ Find your way through from the entry to the exit

INSTRUCTIONS

Find your way through the maze by following the white corridors and not crossing over the black walls.

MENTAL PROCESSES

Mazes are one of the oldest types of puzzle in existence, featuring in Greek mythology that dates back 3,000 years or more. While large, physical labyrinths can be challenging due to issues of orientation and keeping track of location, paper mazes are much simpler. In most mazes there is not much reasoning involved beyond simple guesswork, although certainly if solving without writing in the maze then you will also need steady visual concentration and a good memory so as to avoid repeating the same, dead-end path. Some tactics can come into play by making assumptions about how the maze is designed, such as that it may be much easier to solve in reverse, but many solvers would consider this 'cheating'.

Expert solving time
8 MINUTES

SOLVING TUTOR

1 MINUTE

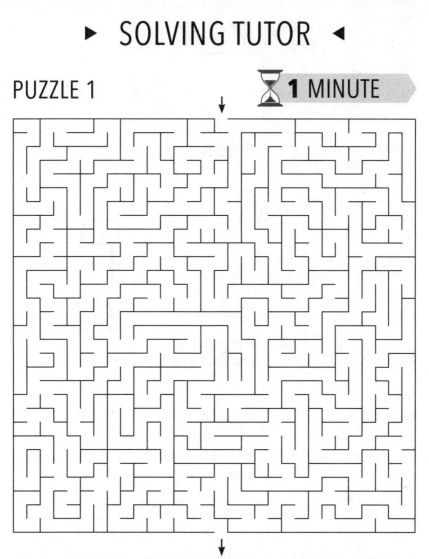

▶ If a maze has no way for paths to cross over one another
– such as using bridges or multiple floors – then a simple
solving tactic is to take note of whenever an area is 'sealed
off'. In other words, once an area has been fully enclosed
by either past exploration or the edges of the maze, it no
longer needs to be explored if it does not also include
the exit. Sometimes this can make a maze considerably
easier than it would otherwise be, and it can make it worth
deliberately taking moves towards the edge of the maze in
the hope of being able to block out large parts of the grid.

PUZZLE 2

PUZZLE 3

In this maze, paths can cross over and under each other by using the marked bridges.

SUDOKU

+ Place digits without repeats in rows, columns or boxes

INSTRUCTIONS

Place a digit from 1 to 6 (or whatever the width of the grid is) into each empty square, so that no digit repeats in any row, column or bold-lined box.

3	4	6	2	1	5
5	2	1	3	6	4
6	3	5	4	2	1
4	1	2	5	3	6
2	6	4	1	5	3
1	5	3	6	4	2

MENTAL PROCESSES

Sudoku is perhaps the most well-known of all logic pencil puzzles. The puzzle hits the sweet spot of challenge where it rarely feels completely trivial, and yet is not usually so tricky that it defies (eventual) solving. Combined with the innate satisfaction found in filling in every empty square, it's a very satisfying puzzle to complete. Despite its simple rules, it can conceal a hugely varied range of logic, with dozens of different solving techniques that can be called upon to help make progress.

Expert solving time
25 MINUTES

SOLVING TUTOR ◄

PUZZLE 1 (1-6)

⏳ **2 MINUTES**

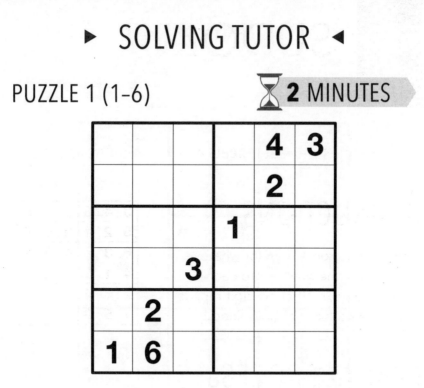

▶ The most basic sudoku deduction is to look for a digit that can only fit in one place in a region (i.e. a row, column or box). For example, in the 3×2 box on the middle left of this grid there is only one place that the '1' can fit.

▶ The opposite deduction, to look for a square in a region that can only contain one, single digit, can be considerably harder to spot, and is one reason why solvers often write small 'pencil mark' candidate numbers into each square to show which digits can fit where. Care must be taken, however, not to write *so many* pencil marks into a grid that you are no longer able to see the wood for the trees!

▶ Check for intersections. If a digit is constrained to only one row or column of a particular box, then it *cannot* be anywhere else in that row or column. This is a powerful elimination technique, so when you observe such a combination it is useful to make a pencil note of it.

► SOLVING TUTOR ◄

6 MINUTES

7			1				9
	6		8			1	
		4	5		2		
		1		8			
9	1	8			7	4	2
		2		9			
		1	2		9		
	4		6			3	
5			9				7

► When a set of 'n' squares within a region contains only 'n' different digits, those digits can be eliminated from anywhere else in the region. For example, the central box can only have a '3', '5' and '6' in its central row, which guarantees that the other two empty squares in the box *cannot* contain those three digits.

► The reverse of the above logic can also be used, when a set of 'n' different digits can only be placed into 'n' different squares in a region. In this case, you can eliminate any other candidate digits as possibilities from those squares. For example, consider

4 7 8 9	1 3 5	1 3 4 5 7
4 5 7	2 7 8	2 4 7 8 9
6	2 4 5	2 4 7

the potential grid situation shown to the right here. The two shaded squares are the only two squares to contain '1' and '3', so they *must* use these two squares. You can therefore eliminate all other options from the two shaded squares.

PUZZLE 3 (1–9)

 **7** MINUTES

	1						4	
4	3		1	9	2		5	6
	9		3	1	4	7		
	4		8		9	3		
	8		2	6	7	1		
2	7		5	3	1		6	4
	6						9	

PUZZLE 4 (1–9)

 **10** MINUTES

6		4		5		8		9
	1		8		6		5	
5		3				6		7
	4						8	
3								5
	7						4	
1		2				4		6
	3		2		7		9	
7		9		1		3		8

NUMBER DARTS

+ Find the set of digits that sum to the given number
+ Pick exactly one digit from each ring of the dartboard

INSTRUCTIONS

Find the set of numbers that sum to a given target, by choosing exactly one number from each ring of the dartboard. Repeat for each of the given values.

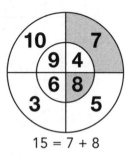

$$15 = 7 + 8$$

MENTAL PROCESSES

Try solving without making pencil notes, using your memory to keep track instead, and this puzzle becomes much more rewarding. It is not only a great test of simple mental arithmetic, but also of your ability to keep track of multiple results in your head. You can also use the results of each addition to choose a sensible guess for your next attempt, if you haven't yet found the answer. If you aren't used to this sort of process, it can seem very tricky to start with – but with a little bit of practice, you soon get much better at it.

Expert solving time
30 MINUTES

PUZZLE 1

⏳ **3** MINUTES

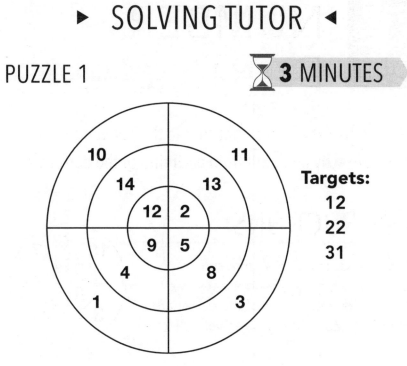

Targets:
12
22
31

Pick one digit from each ring, so that they sum to one of the totals given. Repeat for each total.

▶ Your mental arithmetic may be strong enough to solve this puzzle almost at a glance, but if not then approach it logically, as per the other puzzles in this book. First, look at the range of numbers in each ring. Is one particularly big, or particularly small? Small numbers are clearly more likely to be used for very low targets, and big numbers for very high targets. Look at the numbers in the other rings, and consider how likely these 'outlier' numbers are to be used for each target total. It may be that numbers are so small or so big they can be ignored entirely for certain totals.

▶ You can try adding up the largest numbers from each ring. How close are they to the biggest required total? It may be easier to try subtracting from that total and looking for numbers that differ by that amount, for large targets.

PUZZLE 2

5 MINUTES

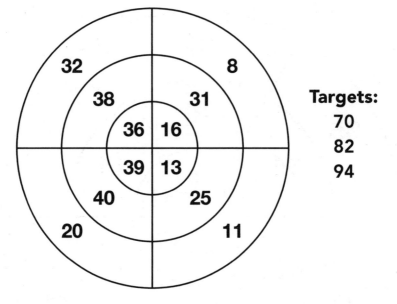

Targets:
70
82
94

PUZZLE 3

8 MINUTES

Targets:
75
112
124

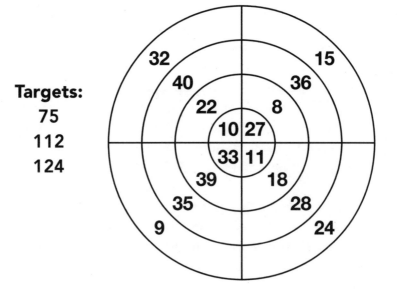

PUZZLE 4

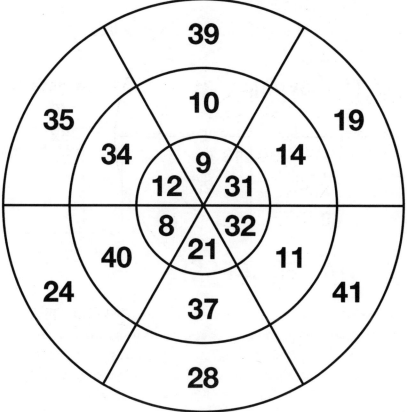

Targets:
53
79
92

SHAPE COUNTING

+ How many of a particular shape can you count?

INSTRUCTIONS

How many rectangles (including squares as well) can you count in the given picture? Count all sizes of rectangle, including the large one around the outside of the puzzle.

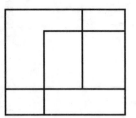

12 rectangles

MENTAL PROCESSES

Puzzles of this type can appear quite overwhelming. Once you start counting, so many shapes start to be observed that it can be hard to keep track. You might choose to try and remember which shapes you've already counted, or you might try to outline them. Both techniques are problematic, and – like many tasks in life – a more logical, step-by-step approach will hugely simplify these puzzles, as is described on the following page. Therefore taking the time to stop and think about how best to approach a seemingly fiddly problem such as this is time well spent.

Expert solving time
15 MINUTES

PUZZLE 1

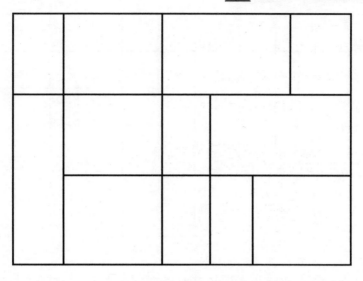

▶ The best way to tackle this type of puzzle is to break it down geometrically in some way. You create a series of much smaller, more tractable counting tasks that you then simply add up once finished.

▶ One easy method is to consider only the top-left-hand corner of each shape. Start at the top-left corner of the grid, and count the number of rectangles which have that precise corner as their *top left* corner. Then continue for every corner in the grid that can be a top-left corner of a rectangle, and count how many possible rectangles can use *that* corner as its top-left corner. Finally, add up all these counts – and you're done. For the example, the total of 12 can be arrived at by counting rectangles from each corner as shown:

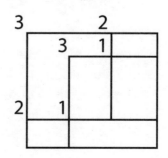

► SOLVING TUTOR ◄

PUZZLE 2 ⏳ 3   PUZZLE 3 ⏳ 3

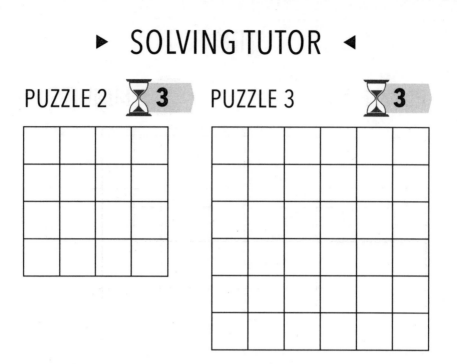

Sometimes a more mathematical approach is called for. First, let's consider the situation where we only count squares:

▶ We know that a 1×1 grid has one square. Next, if you imagine subdividing it with two crossing lines then it is easy to see that a 2×2 grid adds a further 4 (i.e. 2^2) squares to this total. Next, a 3×3 grid will add a further 9 (i.e. 3^2) squares to this total, and so on. So at each increase in grid size to a grid of size $n×n$, we add on n^2 more squares. Therefore the 4×4 grid has $1^2 + 2^2 + 3^2 + 4^2 = 30$ squares.

Adding in rectangles is similar, but a little more complex:

▶ A 1×1 grid still has 1 square, but a 2×2 grid has not just 4 further squares but also 4 1×2 or 2×1 rectangles, for a total of 9 shapes, or $(1 + 2)^2$. If you now count the number of shapes in a 3×3 grid, you'll find that it is $(1 + 2 + 3)^2 = 36$. For a 4×4 grid, it is $(1 + 2 + 3 + 4)^2 = 100$, and so on.

PUZZLE 4

FENCES

+ Draw a single loop which visits every dot exactly once
+ Only horizontal and vertical lines can be used

INSTRUCTIONS

Use horizontal and vertical lines to join neighbouring pairs of dots, forming a single loop which travels in and out of every dot once each. The loop cannot cross over itself, or revisit any dot.

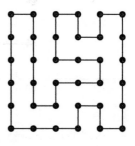

MENTAL PROCESSES

Solving fences puzzles typically involves alternating between both local and global constraints, mixing small step-by-step deductions with more general 'how does it all connect together' observations. This can mirror solving problems in life more generally, where it's important not to lose sight of the principle goal while still simultaneously making sure that you are paying attention to the details too.

Expert solving time
30 MINUTES

PUZZLE 1

⏳ **3** MINUTES

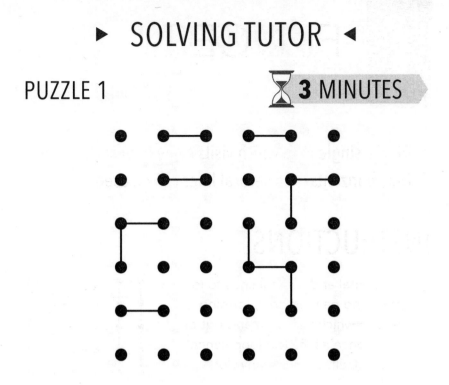

► Start by looking at the corners. The loop has to visit every dot, so it must travel both in and out of each corner. There is only one dot it can connect to from each corner dot, so you can draw in eight path segments straight away.

► The loop visits every dot once, so there must be exactly two lines connected to each dot. There are some dots which already have one line connected but only one remaining other dot they can connect to. Draw these in.

► There are also some dots with no connected lines that only have two other dots they can connect to, so these forced lines can be drawn in too.

► Remember to think about how connecting dots might break the puzzle by creating a loop that doesn't visit every square. For example, this logic can be used at the top left of the puzzle to expand the existing loop fragment.

► SOLVING TUTOR ◄

PUZZLE 2

⏳ **7 MINUTES**

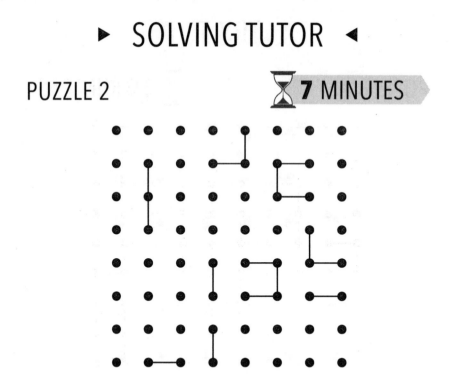

► When solving, remember that all dots must be connected. Any move which leaves one or more dots in a 'dead end', or more generally leaves a dot with insufficient possible connections, must be wrong. For example, the fifth dot on the top row must connect to its right because otherwise it would create a disconnected dot to its right.

► You may at some point when solving a puzzle reach a stage where you can't spot any immediate further deductions. When this happens, try taking a step back and thinking about how the entire loop might be shaped.

► If you are still stuck after considering how the overall loop might connect, then one tactic is to simply pick a dot where there are only two options and guess. It's best to choose a dot in a corner or other confined area that you can see will immediately force other deductions once placed. Circle your guess and then cross or otherwise mark subsequent deductions, so you can undo them if necessary.

PUZZLE 3

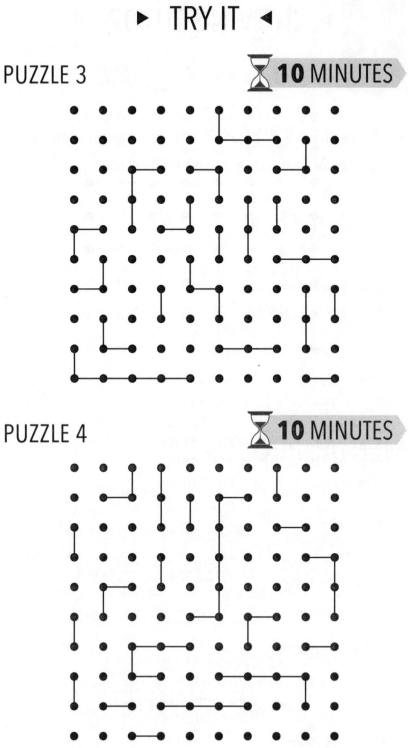

PUZZLE 4

NO FOUR IN A ROW

+ Place either an 'X' or an 'O' into every empty square
+ No lines of four or more can be made in any direction

INSTRUCTIONS

Place 'X' or 'O' into each empty square without creating any lines of four or more identical symbols in any direction, including diagonally. Some symbols are already given. Note that there is no requirement to have equal numbers of both types of symbol.

X	X	O	X	O	O
X	X	X	O	X	O
O	O	X	O	O	O
X	O	O	O	X	X
O	O	X	X	O	X
X	X	O	X	O	O

MENTAL PROCESSES

Despite its simplicity, this puzzle can be remarkably challenging. Even if the logic required is sometimes straightforward, it can often be remarkably hard to spot the 'next move'. Horizontal and vertical lines are reasonably easy to see, but diagonal lines can end up camouflaged in among the many other symbols. It's a great puzzle for practicing your ability to focus and work through a task in an organized way.

Expert solving time
20 MINUTES

► SOLVING TUTOR ◄

PUZZLE 1

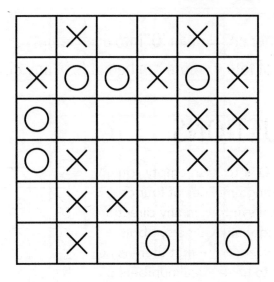

► Solving this puzzle is about paying attention and making step-by-step deductions. One way to solve is by focusing on one of the two symbols first, then scanning for all horizontal and vertical lines of three symbols with a space on either end. You can immediately draw the opposite symbol on the end of these. Similarly, you can then check for diagonal lines which work in the same way, remembering to check both directions of diagonal.

► Slightly harder to spot are lines of four squares where three identical symbols are already placed but the gap is *within* the three shapes, rather than at either end. You might need to scan more slowly to spot these, at least until you have solved a few puzzles. Diagonals can be particularly tricky.

► Keep applying these basic types of deduction repeatedly, swapping symbol each time you get stuck. That's all that's required to solve this first puzzle.

PUZZLE 2

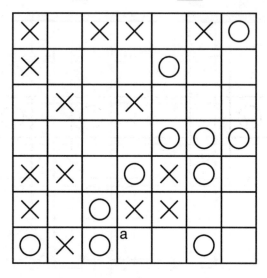

▶ At some point in any solve you may reach a point with no further easy deductions to be made. One tactic for getting started again might be to guess, which would after all give you a 50% chance of being correct. But often a better tactic is to note that you *know* there is only one solution to the puzzle. Given this, you can make deductions on this basis – any grid state which could be changed without affecting any other part of the puzzle *must* be wrong.

▶ Look at the square labelled 'a' above. It is *impossible* for the contents of that square to be forced to be either an 'X' or an 'O' *unless* the square to its right is an 'O'. This is because there has to be a line of three of a shape running up to it to force the opposite shape, and this can only be a horizontal line of 'O's from the right. So you can place an 'O' into the square to its right since without it the puzzle would not have a unique solution – and then once that's placed, you can be certain that the 'a' square is an 'X'.

► TRY IT ◄

PUZZLE 3

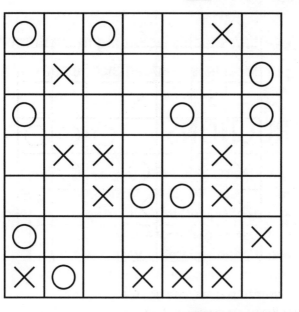

PUZZLE 4

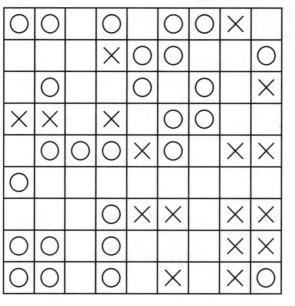

HANJIE

+ Shade certain squares, according to the number clues
+ Each puzzle reveals a hidden picture once solved

INSTRUCTIONS

Shade some squares according to the given clue numbers. The clues provide, in reading order from left to right or top to bottom, the length of every run of consecutive shaded squares in each row and column. There must be a gap of at least one empty square between each run of shaded squares in the same row or column.

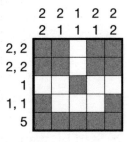

MENTAL PROCESSES

Hanjie puzzles can vary significantly in difficulty, but they always require you to pay close attention to the individual clues in each row and column in order to make progress in the puzzle. As further deductions are made, attention needs to continually shift to other areas of the grid.

Expert solving time
40 MINUTES

PUZZLE 1

 **5 MINUTES**

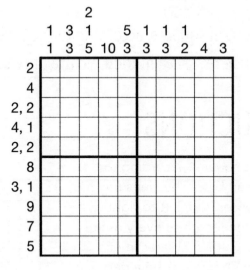

▶ Start by shading all 10 squares in the '10' column.

▶ For the 9, 8 and 7 rows, the central 8, 6 and 4 squares of their rows, respectively, can be shaded. To see why, imagine shading 9/8/7 squares in their leftmost and rightmost possible locations. Any squares shaded in both configurations *must* be shaded no matter what.

▶ Look at the first and second row. The '2' and '4' regions must intersect with the shaded squares from the '10' column. Even though you do not yet know exactly where they are positioned, you can mark 'x's in 7 squares in the '2' row, and 3 squares in the '4' row, to indicate places that can *never* be shaded.

▶ Remember that clues are given in order, so the '4,1' row, for example, must have 4 shaded squares, a gap of 1 or more unshaded squares, and then 1 shaded square.

PUZZLE 2

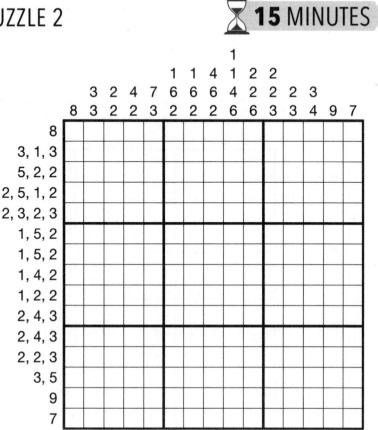

► One way to work out which squares *must* be shaded in a row or column is to shade it with the minimum single space between each 'run', starting first from the left/top and then from the right/bottom. Any squares that are shaded in *both* versions <u>by the same clue number</u> *must* be shaded in the actual solution. For example, consider the '2, 5, 1, 2' row:

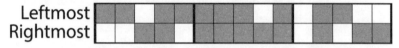

Leftmost
Rightmost

Three of the squares in the '5' are always shaded, so you can shade them for certain in the puzzle, as follows:

2, 5, 1, 2

PUZZLE 3

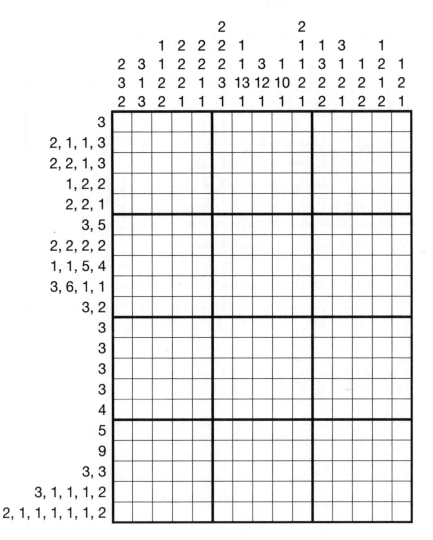

FILLOMINO

+ Divide the grid into regions of varying sizes

INSTRUCTIONS

Draw along some of the grid lines to divide the grid into regions. Regions of the same size cannot touch, except diagonally. Some squares contain given numbers, indicating the size of the region they are in. Not all regions are necessarily indicated by numbers, and

9	9	9	9	9
9	5	9	9	9
1	5	4	4	4
5	5	4	3	2
5	1	3	3	2

there may be multiple numbers for the same region. You may find it helpful to add a number to each square indicating the size of its region, so that you can easily spot touching regions.

MENTAL PROCESSES

Despite the relatively simple rules, Fillomino puzzles can be remarkably complicated. Not all regions are clued, and some may be clued more than once, so the need to deal with this kind of ambiguity is great practice for your brain in handling situations where you have only partial knowledge of the facts.

Expert solving time
20 MINUTES

PUZZLE 1

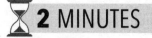

2 MINUTES

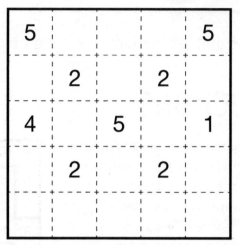

▶ Start by outlining the already-complete '1' region. Next, none of the '2' regions can expand towards one another, since they would then touch, so draw lines on the inner edges of all the '2' regions to indicate this.

▶ The '5' clue at the top left must expand into four further squares, which means it must run to at least the top-middle square. But the same applies to the other '5' clue on the top line, so they must be one and the same region. This fully defines this region, so mark the whole top row as '5's.

▶ The two '2' regions on the second row are now complete since they can no longer expand up. A '1' region is also forced in the centre of the row because the '5' beneath it can't expand into it without touching the other '5' region.

▶ Now expand the '4' region to the bottom-left corner; the need to fit the '2' will force its exact placement. Finally, the remaining '5' clue must now expand to its right, to avoid creating two touching '1' regions.

PUZZLE 2

⧗ **4 MINUTES**

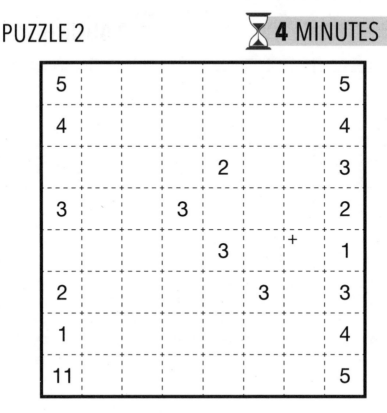

5							5
4							4
				2			3
3			3				2
				3		+	1
2					3		3
1							4
11							5

▶ Start by expanding all of the clues in the rightmost column. All of them can be fully placed. Next, repeat with the clues in the left column, working up and down the column until all except the '11' are complete.

▶ There are twelve squares in the area where the '11' must go, so you can't be certain of its exact placement. Instead, consider the square marked with a '+'. It cannot be a '1', or a '2', or a '3' because in each case it would touch another region of the same size. It must therefore be a '4'. Mark it in, and complete the '4' region.

▶ Now complete the '2' region, forcing a '1' region above. The '3's must now join, to leave space for the '11' region.

50

PUZZLE 3

14 MINUTES

				5	5	7		
		12		6	6		7	8
	4			7	7			
				8	8			7
5	4			12	12	7		
	5		5		2		3	3
				2			4	4
6		6			2		5	5
7		7		2			13	
8		8			2	5		5
								4
			1		13			5
				12		1		
8			1		13			5
12				12				13

TENTS

+ Place a tent next to each tree, so tents don't touch

INSTRUCTIONS

Draw a tent in certain empty squares, so each tent is attached to exactly one tree. Also, each tree must be attached to exactly one tent. Tents must be in a square immediately above, below, to the left or to the right of their attached tree. Trees cannot be added or removed.

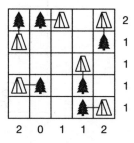

Two tents cannot be placed in touching squares, including diagonally touching squares. Numbers outside the grid give the exact number of tents in certain rows and columns.

MENTAL PROCESSES

Due to the requirement that tents can't touch, these puzzles tend to be quite constricted – so after a few moves, often the rest of the puzzle is heavily forced. Therefore, if you get stuck, it's a puzzle that particularly rewards intelligent guessing.

Expert solving time
15 MINUTES

PUZZLE 1

⌛ **2 MINUTES**

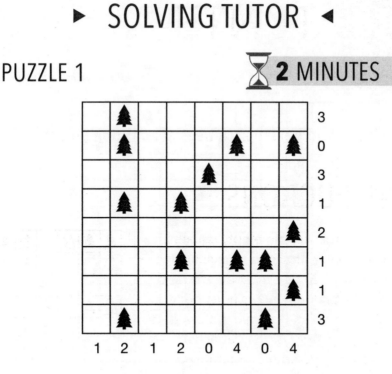

▶ Start by marking an 'x' in every square in the '0' row and columns, so you don't forget these must remain empty.

▶ There is now only one way to place four tents in the rightmost column without them touching or using a tree twice.

▶ Don't forget to mark 'x's around each placed tent, including diagonally, to make clear which squares are still available.

▶ Work out which tree each placed tent connects to. The topmost tree in the rightmost column must connect up, for example, while the topmost tree in the penultimate column must connect to its right. Are there now any trees with only one possible square for their tent to be placed in?

▶ Keep track of which rows and columns are filled while solving, as for example two '1' rows will now be after following these steps. Mark more 'x's in these rows too.

► SOLVING TUTOR ◄

PUZZLE 2

⏳ **5 MINUTES**

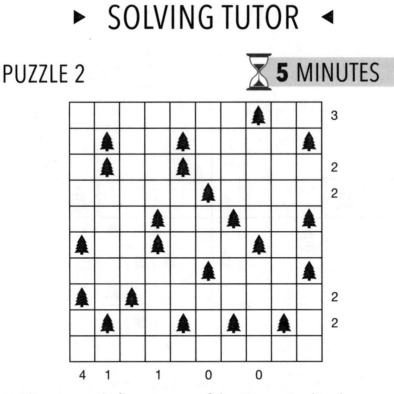

► There are only five squares of the '4' required in the first column that can have a tent in, but only one of the two near the top can be used (in order to prevent trees touching) – so the lower three can be marked in.

► With these three tents placed, and linked to their trees, there is now only one valid place for a tent in the second column. It must go directly above the topmost tree.

► Consider the tree four down in the sixth column. As a zero column, its tent must be to its left or right, but if it went to the left it would mean there was no way to solve the tree immediately to its top left. Therefore its tent must attach to its right. This leads to a chain of further deductions.

► Now note similarly that the tree five down in the fourth column cannot have its tent above it, since it would prevent a tree from having a tent. So it must go to its right.

PUZZLE 3

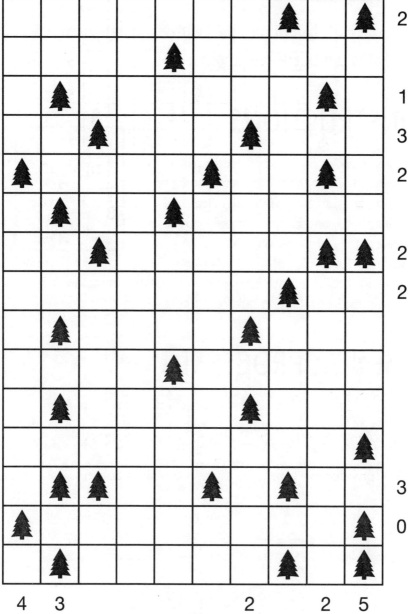

NUMBER LINK

+ Join each pair of numbers with a separate path
+ Paths can't cross one another

INSTRUCTIONS

Draw a series of separate paths, each connecting a pair of identical numbers. No more than one path can enter any square, and paths can only travel horizontally or vertically between squares. Each pair of numbers must

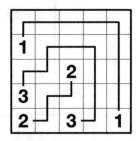

have exactly one path between them. Note there is *no* requirement that all squares are used.

MENTAL PROCESSES

Number link puzzles combine logical deductions with an ability to visualize how the solution might look. Typically they are solved more by an instinctive 'feel' for how the numbers must connect than a step-by-step reasoned approach, and certainly in many puzzles it will help to make sensible guesses in order to speed your way to the final solution.

Expert solving time
8 MINUTES

► SOLVING TUTOR ◄

PUZZLE 1

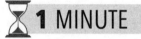
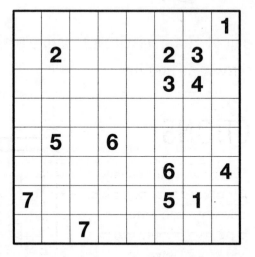

► The '7's are in the corner, so no path can come between them. Draw their connecting path so it travels directly via the corner – you can be certain of this route because you know the puzzle has a unique solution, remembering that there is no rule that all squares are used. If it did not go directly via the corner then (with nothing else to fill the empty space in the corner) there would be multiple solutions to the puzzle. You can therefore be confident that this placement is forced by the rest of the puzzle.

► Using similar logic, draw a partial path that passes around and behind the '2' at the top left. This must be there because otherwise, with similar logic, there would not be a unique solution – the '2' would have to meander here.

► In an almost identical way, the '4' must travel via the bottom-right corner. Nothing else can reach it, and if the '1' went there it would be an optional part of its path – and there can't be optional parts with a unique solution.

SOLVING TUTOR

PUZZLE 2

⏳ **2 MINUTES**

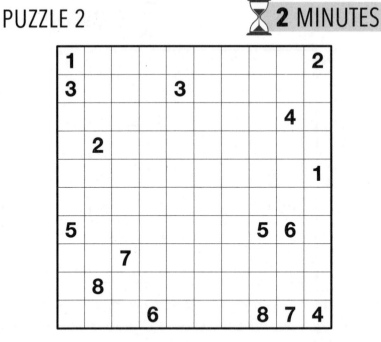

▶ A path must travel in and then out of the bottom-left corner, without connecting to the '8'.

▶ The '7' and '4' at the bottom right must both extend upwards, at least one square for the '7' and two for the '4'.

▶ At this point the fastest approach is to eyeball the grid and see if you can imagine how the paths probably go. For example, the '3's might connect in a straight line, and the '1' would then travel around that '3' path and hook back behind the leftmost '2' to then run straight across to the '1'. Ah... but wait, that can't work since this would trap the '4' on its own in the top half of the grid. Oh, but I can tweak that placement by looping the '1' up and over the uppermost '4' before connecting it to the '1'. And then the '4's can run down the rightmost side of the grid to connect. You can then draw this in, and continue using similar steps.

PUZZLE 3

 **5** MINUTES

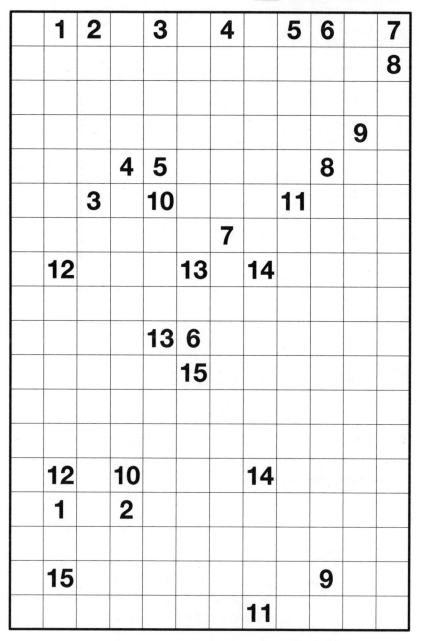

SHIKAKU

+ Divide the grid into rectangles
+ Each rectangle must contain a number equal to its size

INSTRUCTIONS

Draw along some grid lines to divide the grid into a set of rectangles and/or squares, so that each region contains one number, and every number is contained within one region. The number in each region must be exactly equal to the number of squares contained in that region.

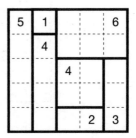

MENTAL PROCESSES

Shikaku, also known as 'Rectangles' or 'Cell Block', involves making step-by-step deductions to gradually fill the grid with the requisite rectangles and squares. Careful counting is usually all that's required, along with a small amount of persistence to search for the best next place to draw a line.

Expert solving time
18 MINUTES

► SOLVING TUTOR ◄

PUZZLE 1

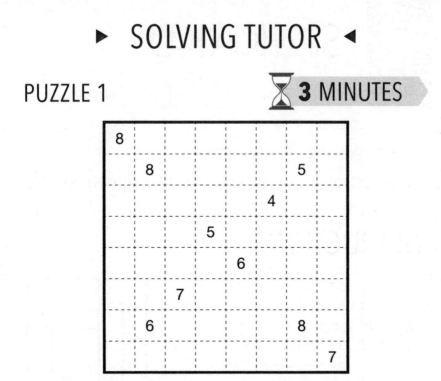

▶ Start by looking at the top-right square. It has to form part of a region, and the only way to reach it is with a long 8×1 rectangle from the '8' at the very top left of the puzzle.

▶ The '7' clue at the bottom-right can only have two possible solutions – either a vertical 1×7 rectangle, or a horizontal 7×1 rectangle. However, if it was a horizontal rectangle then the bottom-left square of the grid would be impossible to reach by any region, so it *must* be vertical.

▶ The grid square immediately below the top-left '8' clue can now only be reached by the '8' clue in the second column, and similarly there is only one region that can reach the bottom-left square in the grid, and one region that can reach the penultimate square in the bottom row.

▶ Making further progress, even with these observations, is tricky. Try placing the remaining '7' horizontally, and you will reach a contradiction – so it must be vertical.

► SOLVING TUTOR ◄

PUZZLE 2

⏳ **5** MINUTES

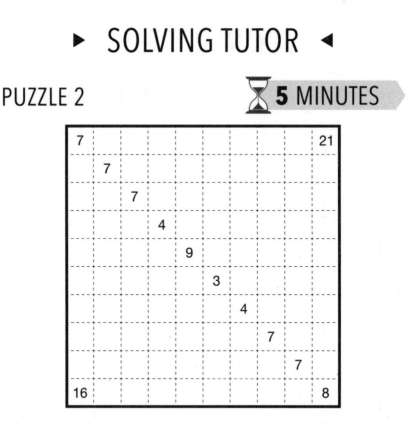

▶ This puzzle may not appear to have an obvious starting point, since the clues along the main diagonal mostly have many possible placements.

▶ When you aren't sure where to make progress, look at both the most visually constrained clues – for example those in corners, or pressed against one or more regions – and also those with the largest value, since these are also often similarly restricted in their possibilities.

▶ In this case, the puzzle can be solved by considering the '21' clue at the top right. No matter how it is solved, it must cover at least a 3×3 square in that corner, since it is either 3×7 or 7×3. With that 3×3 area marked in, consider the square four down in the rightmost column. It now cannot be reached by *any* clue other than the '21' itself, so the '21' must be a vertical 3×7 rectangle.

PUZZLE 3

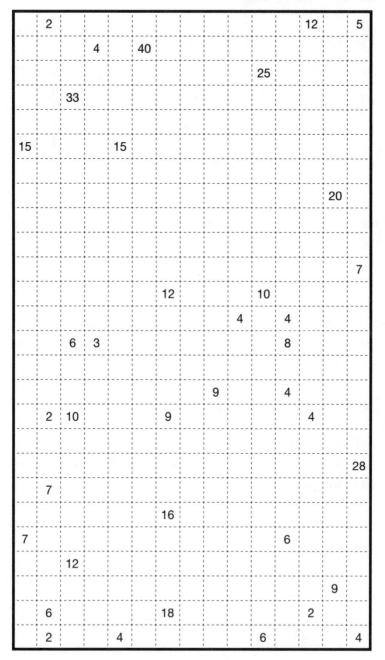

YIN YANG

+ Place a black or white circle in every square
+ All circles of the same colour must connect together
+ No 2×2 areas of the same colour are allowed

INSTRUCTIONS

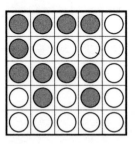

Every empty square must have either a black or a white circle added to it. All circles of the same colour must form a single continuous region, where you can travel from any circle of that colour to any other of the same colour while stepping only via circles of that colour. Steps can only be horizontally or vertically between touching squares. In addition, there may not be any 2×2 areas of the same colour.

MENTAL PROCESSES

Yin yang puzzles have a certain set of suitable logical rules that can be applied to help solve them, but in many puzzles there comes a point where you also need to visualize the puzzle as a whole and attempt to work out how it all connects.

Expert solving time
30 MINUTES

PUZZLE 1

⧗ **3 MINUTES**

▶ There are only two areas: one that's all white, and one that's all black. This means that there can only be two regions on the outer border – one length of black circles, and the remainder all of white circles. Were this not the case, it wouldn't be possible for each region to remain connected. In this puzzle, this observation allows you to immediately fill in every edge circle except for one.

▶ Now use the fact that there cannot be any 2×2 areas of a single colour to fill in several more squares with an opposing colour.

▶ All the circles of each colour must be connected, so the black circles must connect from the second column to the others in the grid. Expand them around until they connect.

▶ Keep applying similar logic until the puzzle is complete.

PUZZLE 2

 **5 MINUTES**

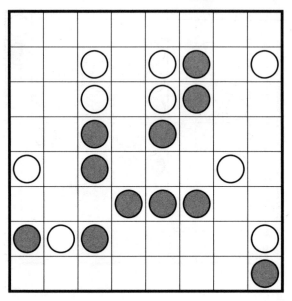

▶ Start by using the observation that there can be no more than two 'runs' of colour around the edge. This lets you solve all but one of the edge squares.

▶ Another handy observation when solving yin yang puzzles is that you can never have a chequerboard pattern in any 2×2 square. In other words, neither of the following patterns can ever form part of a valid solution:

   or

If either of these appeared then you would have at least three regions in the puzzle, not two (i.e. one of each type), since if e.g. the white pieces in either pattern connected then they would have to disconnect the two black circles from one another, no matter how the white circles connect.

▶ TRY IT ◀

PUZZLE 3

⏳ **10** MINUTES

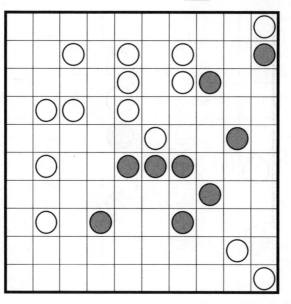

PUZZLE 4

⏳ **12** MINUTES

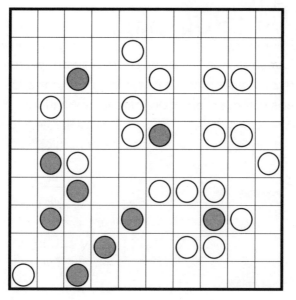

HITORI

+ Shade certain squares so numbers don't repeat
+ Shaded squares may not touch
+ All unshaded squares must form a single region

INSTRUCTIONS

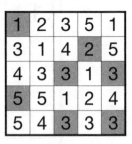

Shade certain squares, so that no unshaded number or letter repeats within any row or column. Shaded squares cannot touch, except diagonally. Also, all of the unshaded squares must form a single connected area, travelling left/right/up/down between unshaded squares.

MENTAL PROCESSES

When you first solve a hitori puzzle your focus will mainly be on remembering the various rules, but once you become more familiar they are all about careful observation. You will start to look for particular patterns, and may learn to scan ahead to consider the inference of certain placements.

Expert solving time
25 MINUTES

PUZZLE 1

 **5 MINUTES**

6	7	3	4	6	1	6
7	2	5	7	1	7	4
4	3	6	1	6	2	6
1	7	6	7	4	2	5
3	6	3	5	3	4	7
7	7	1	2	6	5	3
2	1	4	3	1	6	7

► The '1' in the second row must be unshaded, since if it were shaded then both the '7's next to it would have to be unshaded – but then you would have two unshaded identical numbers on the same row, which is forbidden. Draw a circle around the '1' to make a note of this, then shade in the '1' at the bottom of the same column since you now already have a '1' in this column.

► Circle the numbers touching the shaded '1', which in turn will allow you to shade both the '6's in column five. Then repeat with the squares next to the '6's, which leads to the result shown to the right.

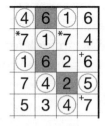

► Now note this top-right area. One of the two '7's marked with a '*' *must* be shaded, so both the '6' and '7' marked with a '+' must be *unshaded* in order to keep all of the unshaded squares in one single, connected region.

► SOLVING TUTOR ◄

PUZZLE 2

⏳ **8 MINUTES**

4	7	1	6	3	8	3	4
2	1	3	7	5	7	4	6
5	4	1	8	1	6	5	3
1	3	4	3	8	7	6	7
6	2	2	1	2	3	8	4
1	3	8	1	7	7	2	5
3	8	6	5	6	2	1	6
1	6	5	3	4	7	7	2

► Note the two touching '2's in the fifth row. One of these must be shaded which means the other must be unshaded. This means the '2' further along the fifth row must be shaded, which forces its touching '1' and '7' squares to be unshaded, and then *their* touching '1' and '7' squares to be shaded in turn. This means the '6' immediately beneath must be unshaded, to keep all unshaded areas connected.

► After some further steps, the '5' at the top-right ends up shaded, as shown to the right. At this point, note the '7' marked with a '*'. If it was unshaded, the two '7's marked with a '+' would be shaded. This in turn would 'seal off' the

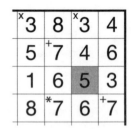

top-right area, due to the '3's marked with 'x's. One of these would have to be shaded, and whichever one it is the area is sealed. So the square marked with a '*' must be shaded.

▶ TRY IT ◀

PUZZLE 3

⧗ **12** MINUTES

4	H	A	E	B	2	D	2	A	C	F	6	7	3	1	9	1
2	8	9	1	C	H	C	5	7	9	8	9	G	E	D	E	B
6	3	6	E	9	2	1	2	A	D	F	8	B	7	1	5	8
E	8	8	D	6	7	1	A	1	B	5	B	C	4	9	3	2
3	6	3	2	E	3	7	2	9	H	F	A	B	B	1	G	4
7	8	G	3	G	F	A	H	9	1	9	5	C	E	4	C
4	9	4	2	1	3	5	2	6	G	F	H	B	4	C	E	A
G	D	H	7	5	1	2	8	D	4	D	F	7	9	E	B	C
F	B	A	G	5	9	3	3	G	H	H	D	2	8	C	6
B	G	2	7	F	G	3	C	5	6	B	E	B	H	A	1	9
5	2	6	4	7	9	H	1	B	3	G	H	E	D	A	H	H
A	D	B	6	3	1	H	F	4	F	E	C	8	6	7	D	9
9	F	E	G	4	2	4	7	B	8	7	5	6	1	A	A	H
C	8	D	A	B	1	B	1	H	G	9	4	2	E	2	E	3
5	E	5	F	D	2	8	4	C	B	H	7	9	A	A	6	1
B	8	F	C	H	C	G	2	E	2	7	D	1	5	6	8	D
D	1	7	9	C	E	A	6	C	G	2	G	3	B	5	F	7

DAY
17 KAKURO

+ Place numbers so that they sum to the given totals
+ No number can repeat within any single sum

INSTRUCTIONS

Place a number from 1 to 9 into each empty square, so that each continuous horizontal or vertical run of white squares adds up to the total given to its left or at its top, respectively. No number can repeat within any run.

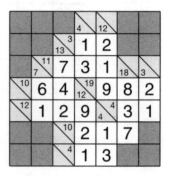

MENTAL PROCESSES

When you first encounter kakuro it appears to consist mainly of mathematical calculations, but once you start to become more familiar the actual amount of adding up starts to become a much smaller component of the puzzle. There are only a certain range of possible sums, and they start to become more and more familiar. After a few puzzles, you'll know a core set of sums off by heart without having to think.

Expert solving time
25 MINUTES

SOLVING TUTOR

PUZZLE 1

 **3 MINUTES**

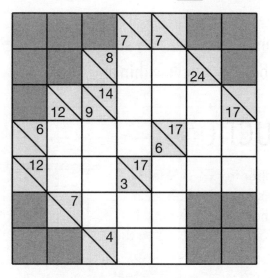

▶ The solution to '3', at the bottom of the puzzle, must be 1+2. There is a '4' clue crossing it and, since a number can't repeat within a kakuro sum, the answer to that clue must be 1+3. The only number they have in common is 1, so the square where the '3' and '4' clues intersect must contain 1. This also allows you to place the 2 and 3 from these two answers.

▶ The same '3' clue intersects a '7' clue, which must have the solution 1+2+4, but that '7' clue itself intersects a '6' clue, which must be 1+2+3. There is already a '2' in the answer, from the '3' clue, and so the only number left in common between the '7' and '6' clues is the 1, so where those two clues intersect there must be a 1. The rest of these clues can then also be completed, since two squares are already placed in each answer.

▶ Continue solving via similar crossing clue deductions.

► SOLVING TUTOR ◄

PUZZLE 2

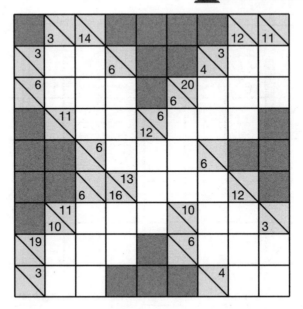

Use these tables to help with some clues in these puzzles:

Clues of length 2:

3: 1,2
4: 1,3
5: 1,4; 2,3
6: 1,5; 2,4
7: 1,6; 2,5; 3,4
8: 1,7; 2,6; 3,5
9: 1,8; 2,7; 3,6; 4,5
10: 1,9; 2,8; 3,7; 4,6
11: 2,9; 3,8; 4,7; 5,6
12: 3,9; 4,8; 5,7
13: 4,9; 5,8; 6,7
14: 5,9; 6,8
15: 6,9; 7,8
16: 7,9
17: 8,9

Clues of length 3:

6: 1,2,3
7: 1,2,4
8: 1,2,5; 1,3,4
9: 1,2,6; 1,3,5; 2,3,4
10: 1,2,7; 1,3,6; 1,4,5; 2,3,5
11: 1,2,8; 1,3,7; 1,4,6; 2,3,6; 2,4,5
12: 1,2,9; 1,3,8; 1,4,7; 1,5,6; 2,3,7; 2,4,6; 3,4,5
13: 1,3,9; 1,4,8; 1,5,7; 2,3,8; 2,4,7; 2,5,6; 3,4,6
14: 1,4,9; 1,5,8; 1,6,7; 2,3,9; 2,4,8; 2,5,7; 3,4,7; 3,5,6
15: 1,5,9; 1,6,8; 2,4,9; 2,5,8; 2,6,7; 3,4,8; 3,5,7; 4,5,6
16: 1,6,9; 1,7,8; 2,5,9; 2,6,8; 3,4,9; 3,5,8; 3,6,7; 4,5,7
17: 1,7,9; 2,6,9; 2,7,8; 3,5,9; 3,6,8; 4,5,8; 4,6,7
18: 1,8,9; 2,7,9; 3,6,9; 3,7,8; 4,5,9; 4,6,8; 5,6,7
19: 2,8,9; 3,7,9; 4,6,9; 4,7,8; 5,6,8
20: 3,8,9; 4,7,9; 5,6,9; 5,7,8
21: 4,8,9; 5,7,9; 6,7,8
22: 5,8,9; 6,7,9
23: 6,8,9
24: 7,8,9

▶ TRY IT ◀

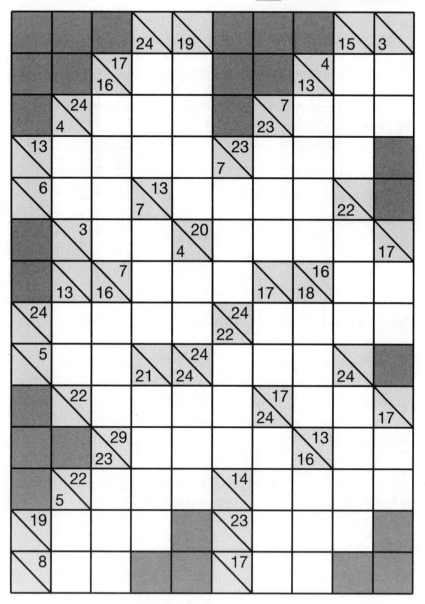

TOUCHY

+ Place letters so they don't repeat in rows or columns
+ Identical letters also cannot touch diagonally

INSTRUCTIONS

Place a letter from the given set into each empty square in such a way that no letter repeats in any row or column. Additionally, identical letters may also not be in diagonally touching squares.

B	F	C	E	A	D
E	A	B	D	F	C
F	D	E	C	B	A
C	B	F	A	D	E
A	E	D	B	C	F
D	C	A	F	E	B

MENTAL PROCESSES

Touchy puzzles involve careful observation, particularly if you are familiar with sudoku since it's very easy to miss the additional implications of the diagonal restrictions. When you get stuck, they reward a careful step-by-step process whereby making smaller 'pencil mark' deductions can help guide you towards the solution – although, like most puzzles, these should be made prudently so as not to overwhelm the grid with information, and thus avoiding a 'can't see the wood for the trees' type of problem.

Expert solving time
30 MINUTES

PUZZLE 1 (A–F)

⏳ **2 MINUTES**

	A		D		
		B	E		
		C	A		
	B		C		

▶ Start by looking for the rows or columns which are most constrained. A row or column between two other fairly full rows or columns is probably the best place to start, due to the diagonal restrictions. Along with the regular row and column constraints, each placed letter prevents the same letter from appearing in any of the up to 8 neighbouring squares.

▶ In this puzzle, consider the third row down. There is only one place that an 'A' can be placed. Once placed, there is now only one place 'A' can go in the fifth row; and then the first row; and then the last 'A', in the bottom row.

▶ Now consider the columns, and notice that in the fifth column there is only one place that the 'E' can fit. You can now place all the remaining 'E's, via similar step-by-step logic to that used for 'A' above.

► SOLVING TUTOR ◄

PUZZLE 2 (A–G)

			E			
D			B			A
	G				B	
			G			
	A				E	
E			C			G
			F			

▶ Small pencil mark notes are often worth making, particularly to note pairs of squares where a particular letter must fit in a row or column. To mark two adjacent squares, try writing a small letter across the join between them. This letter can't then be placed in a square that shares a side with either of the two noted squares.

▶ General solving techniques are similar to those for sudoku. Look for letters that can fit in only one place in a column, and conversely for squares where only one letter can place. More complex sudoku techniques can also be used, although are less likely to be required.

▶ In this particular puzzle, start by completing the central column, then place all but two 'A's and all but two 'E's. Next up, you can place a 'G' in the fifth row, followed by a 'C' in the same row.

▶ TRY IT ◀

PUZZLE 3 (A–G)

 **8** MINUTES

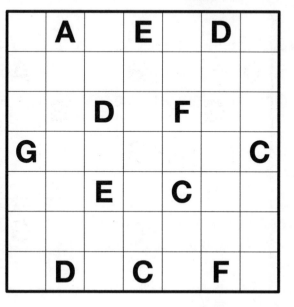

	A		E		D	
		D		F		
G						C
		E		C		
	D		C		F	

PUZZLE 4 (A–H)

 **12** MINUTES

	D					C	
			D	A			
H		C			G		D
	A					F	
	C					H	
F		H			A		B
			F	B			
	H					G	

HASHI / BRIDGES

+ Draw straight-line 'bridges' between 'islands'
+ Each 'island' must have the given number of bridges
+ All bridges must form a single connected network

INSTRUCTIONS

Join circled numbers with horizontal or vertical lines. Each number must have as many lines connected to it as specified by its value. No more than two lines may join any pair of numbers, and no lines may cross. The finished layout must connect all numbers, so you can travel between any pair of numbers by following one or more lines.

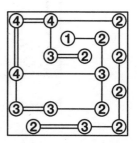

MENTAL PROCESSES

Hashi puzzles require a mix of skills, since you must not only make sure that all of the number clues are fulfilled but also ensure that the all-connected constraint is kept to. In practice, you will work back and forth between the two considerations.

Expert solving time
15 MINUTES

PUZZLE 1

⧗ **2 MINUTES**

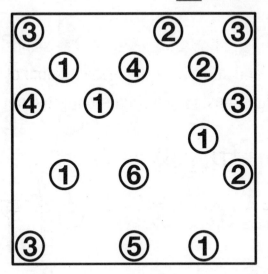

▶ The '1' at the top-left can only connect to its right or down. If it connected down it would join another '1', creating a separate network that couldn't connect to the rest of the puzzle – so it must connect to its right. Similar logic can also be used to connect some of the other '1's too.

▶ Several numbers in the grid have a sufficiently high total that they must have at least one connection in every possible direction. For example, the '3' at the top-left must have at least one connection down and at least one connection to its right, since there cannot be more than two lines joining any given pair of numbers.

▶ Draw in the various lines forced by the deductions above. As you do so, you start to limit the options for other numbers in the grid due to the fact that lines can't cross over one another (or over another number, either). This then in turn allows further deductions to be made.

PUZZLE 2

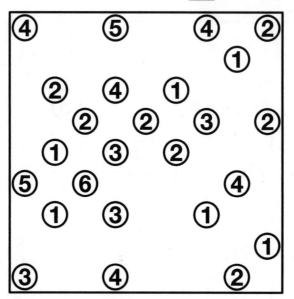

▶ This grid contains four numbers that are already at their maximums, given the other numbers they can connect to directly, so can have two lines connected on all possible sides immediately. These are the '4' at the top left, the '1's at the top right and bottom right, and the '6'.

▶ Consider also the '2' at the top right of the grid. It *must* have a connection to its left because were both of its connections to go straight down then it would form a 'sealed-off' network with the '2' immediately beneath it.

▶ In larger puzzles, it can help to cross out each number once it is fully satisfied. This makes it easier spot numbers which are *nearly* fulfilled, but not quite.

▶ In the puzzle on the next page, you will need to continually consider how to keep the entire network connected as one.

PUZZLE 3

SNAKE

+ Draw a snake that connects the given head and tail
+ Number clues outside the grid must be obeyed

INSTRUCTIONS

Draw a circle in some squares to form a single snake that starts and ends at the given squares. A snake is a path of adjacent squares that does not branch or cross over itself. The snake does not touch itself – not even diagonally, except when turning a corner. Numbers

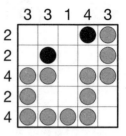

outside the grid specify the number of squares in their row or column that contain part of the snake. Not all numbers are necessarily given.

MENTAL PROCESSES

Snake is relatively unusual in that it often involves guessing to solve, whereby you draw in a possible path and then try to 'tweak' it to fulfil the various requirements. Some snake puzzles do have a more logical path to them, but not all do.

Expert solving time
45 MINUTES

PUZZLE 1

⌛ **3** MINUTES

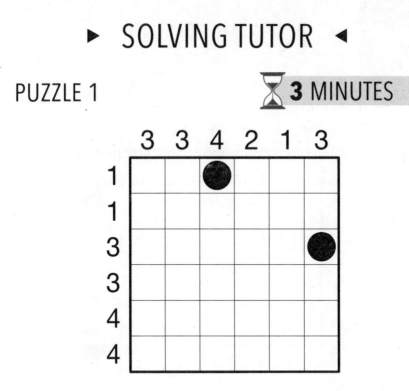

► The '1' rows and columns are of particular interest. The snake must cross over each of these, and then not return – because returning would require a '2' or above. In the special case of the top row, which already has one end of the snake given, this means that the snake path must immediately move downwards – and then again, due to the second row.

► Edge rows and columns are also of interest. Consider the '3's in the two outer columns. These mean the snake can only enter each column once, since it would need a minimum of six squares to enter twice. This is because the snake can't touch itself, so once it reaches an edge it must move at least two further squares along the edge, and therefore each entry and exit from an edge of the grid requires a minimum of three squares. To visit twice would in any case also require at least one empty square between each visit to prevent touching, which can't fit in a 6×6 grid.

PUZZLE 2

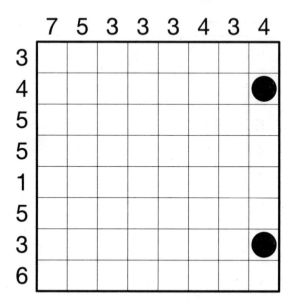

▶ The '1' row divides the grid into two, since once the snake moves across this row it can't cross it again. You therefore know that all '6' squares in the bottom row must be visited shortly after the snake leaves its bottom-right end.

▶ The '3' in the penultimate row either means that the row is crossed twice, or that it is crossed once but that it moves left/right one square while on that row (because one square is already used by the marked snake end). Look to make as many similar observations as possible so you start to limit the ways the snake can be placed.

▶ The '7' in the leftmost column leaves only one square unvisited. Let's try excluding the '1' row. This would force five of the six squares in the bottom-left 2×3 area to be filled, and then the rest of the bottom three rows. The rest of the snake is then forced step by step, and this works.

▶ TRY IT ◀

PUZZLE 3

⏳ **14** MINUTES

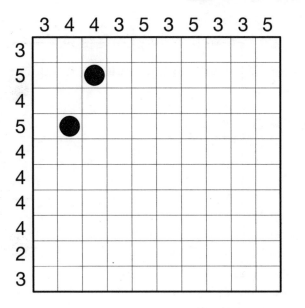

PUZZLE 4

⏳ **20** MINUTES

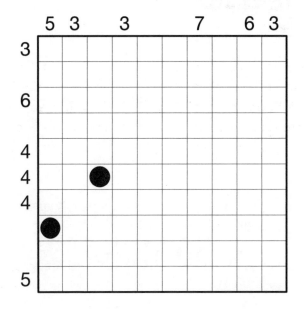

FRAME SUDOKU

+ Place numbers so that they don't repeat in any region
+ Numbers must sum to the values given outside

INSTRUCTIONS

Place a digit from 1 to 9 into each empty square, so that no digit repeats in any row, column or bold-lined 3×3 box. Clue values outside the grid reveal the sum of all of the squares in their row or column between the nearest edge of the puzzle and the first bold line.

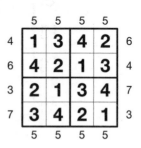

MENTAL PROCESSES

Frame sudoku combines mathematical deductions with standard sudoku reasoning, requiring a mix of different types of deduction. Despite its initial appearance, the puzzles are not intrinsically harder than regular sudoku – and in fact they can be easier, since each frame clue can provide more information than a single standard sudoku clue number.

Expert solving time
35 MINUTES

PUZZLE 1 (1–6)

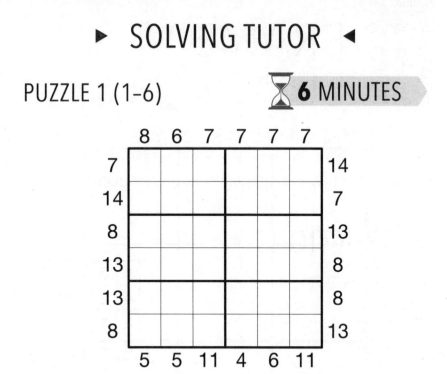

▶ Due to the 3×2 bold-lined regions, in this puzzle the horizontal clues given the sum of the three nearest squares, while the vertical clues give the sum of the two nearest.

▶ Similar logic to that used in kakuro (see day 17) can be used since, due to the standard rules of sudoku prohibiting repeated digits, the possible sums for each total are heavily restricted. The horizontal '7' clues must be 1+2+4, for example.

▶ Consider the top-left square of the grid. The '7' clue horizontally constrains this square to be 1, 2 or 4. If it were 1, the crossing '8' clue could not be solved since it would require 1+7, but only numbers up to six can be placed in this puzzle, and if it were '4' it would require 4+4 which would repeat a digit within a column. So the top-left square must be a 2, and the square immediately beneath it must be a 6.

► SOLVING TUTOR ◄

PUZZLE 2 (1–9)

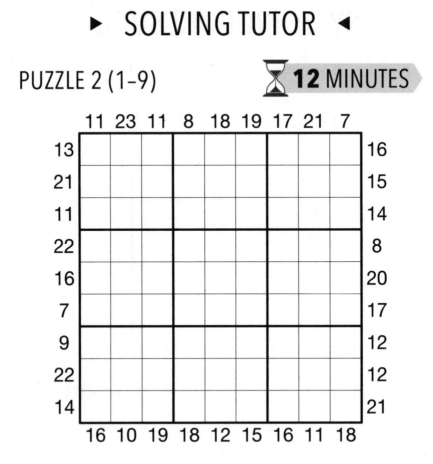

12 MINUTES

▶ In this puzzle, all of the frame clues are the sum of the three nearest squares. Start by looking for clues that are near the lowest and highest possible totals of three squares (6 and 24 respectively), since these will be the most constrained in terms of possible solutions.

▶ Try writing small pencil mark options into some of the more constrained squares. Then look at their crossing clues – these pencil marks options may limit the number of possible solutions to these too. Via a step-by-step series of deductions, you can start to place digits in the grid.

▶ Don't forget to apply sudoku logic – once you have a number placed, it can't also be used to solve another clue in the same row or column.

▶ TRY IT: PRODUCT SUDOKU ◀

The outer values are **products**, not totals, in these two puzzles:

PUZZLE 3 (1–6)

⏳ **5** MINUTES

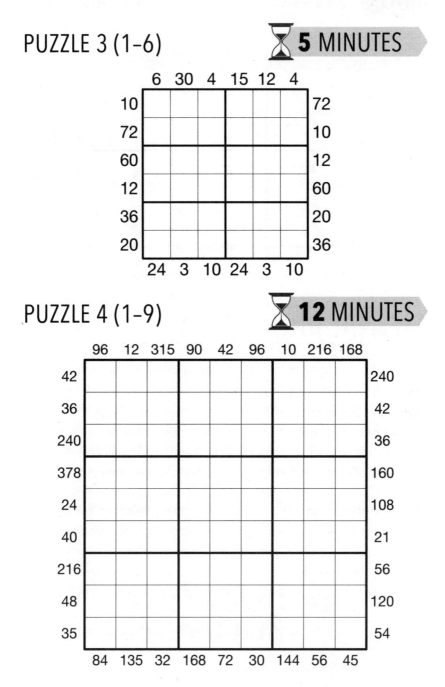

```
        6  30   4  15  12   4
    10 ┌──┬──┬──┬──┬──┬──┐ 72
    72 │  │  │  │  │  │  │ 10
    60 │  │  │  │  │  │  │ 12
    12 │  │  │  │  │  │  │ 60
    36 │  │  │  │  │  │  │ 20
    20 └──┴──┴──┴──┴──┴──┘ 36
       24   3  10  24   3  10
```

PUZZLE 4 (1–9)

⏳ **12** MINUTES

```
         96  12 315  90  42  96  10 216 168
     42 ┌──────────────────────────────┐ 240
     36 │                              │ 42
    240 │                              │ 36
    378 │                              │ 160
     24 │                              │ 108
     40 │                              │ 21
    216 │                              │ 56
     48 │                              │ 120
     35 └──────────────────────────────┘ 54
         84 135  32 168  72  30 144  56  45
```

MINESWEEPER

+ Place mines into certain squares, based on clues

INSTRUCTIONS

Place mines into some empty squares in the grid. Clues in some squares show the number of mines in touching squares – including diagonally. No more than one mine may be placed per square.

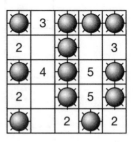

MENTAL PROCESSES

Unlike the version once included with computers running Windows, minesweeper paper puzzles can be solved by logical deduction – as for all the other puzzle types in this book, there's only one solution which fits the given clues. Due to the way each mine is often clued by multiple numbers, solving these puzzles typically requires keeping several constraints in mind all at once, which can be a challenge. A combination of sensible note-taking, combined with a good memory and concentration, is key to solving the harder ones.

Expert solving time
20 MINUTES

▶ SOLVING TUTOR ◀

PUZZLE 1

	2			2
2			3	
		1		
	3		2	
		3		

▶ Start by looking for clues which require all of their touching squares to be filled with mines, such as the '3' clue on the bottom row of this puzzle. These mines can be placed immediately. When a clue has all of its mines placed, cross it out to help you keep track.

▶ Check to see if any further clues have been fully solved by the mines just placed. If they have, mark any empty squares around them with an 'x', to keep track of this. For example, in this puzzle the '2' in the fourth row can now have 'x's marked around it, since the '3' to its bottom-left has been solved.

▶ If you now know that some squares are definitely empty, check again to see if any other mine placements are forced now that there are fewer squares they can fit into.

► SOLVING TUTOR ◄

PUZZLE 2

⏳ **5 MINUTES**

2			3		2	
3			3	1		2
		4		2	2	
	3			2		2
2			3		1	1
	1	1		3		2
1			2			

The puzzle above can be solved using the logic described on the previous page, but what about more complex puzzles?

► A useful tactic is to draw lines to mark a range of squares that a mine *could* be in. For example, if you know that a mine has to be in one of two squares, draw a line spanning those two squares. This will help when solving adjacent clues, since you can then clearly see where some mines must be placed.

► When drawing these lines, it is worth distinguishing between marks that indicate 'exactly '*n*' mines go here' and 'at least '*n*' mines goes here', since they will affect the deductions you can make with them. You could try putting a slash across 'or more' lines, and using '*n*' parallel lines to indicate '*n*' mines.

PUZZLE 3

	2		2		2	
2		2	3	1		2
	2				2	
3	5	3	3			2
			2		2	
3	5		4			2
	2				2	

PUZZLE 4

	2		2		1	2		1
2	4			2			3	2
	4		6				3	
3			5		3		2	
			3			3		1
4		4	2			2		1
	3	3		3	2		2	
3		3			1	1		1
2		2	1		1		1	1

SPIRAL GALAXIES

+ Divide the grid into a set of regions
+ Every region must be symmetrical around a circle

INSTRUCTIONS

Draw along some of the grid lines to divide the grid into a set of regions. Every region must contain exactly one circle, and the region must be symmetrical in such a way that if rotated 180 degrees around the circle it would look exactly the same.

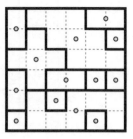

MENTAL PROCESSES

These visual puzzles can mostly be solved via step-by-step logical deduction, but they also benefit from keen observational skills. Region outlines may be complex, and it can require concentration to work out the exact symmetries required. It's also important to avoid accidentally missing possible region layouts, since these can lead to solving mistakes that can be hard to correct.

Expert solving time
35 MINUTES

► SOLVING TUTOR ◄

PUZZLE 1

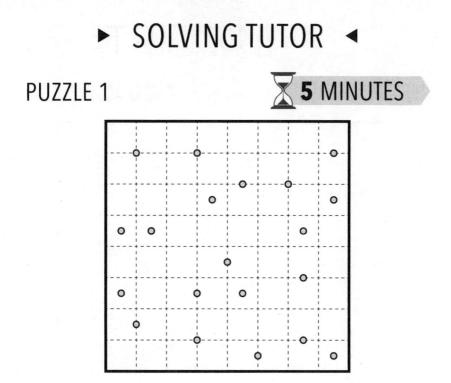

► Regions near the edge of the puzzle, or surrounded by other circles, can be heavily constrained – often some can be placed immediately. Mark these in by drawing their borders, such as for example of the 1×1 region at the bottom-right of the grid, or the 2×2 region at the top left.

► Don't just draw in complete regions, but also border walls. For example, consider the region covered by the circle in the penultimate row of the first and second columns. There is a border above and to the left of the square in the first column, so symmetrical borders must be present in the square in the second column, on the opposite side of the circle. Mark these in.

► As you start to mark more and more regions and borders in, so other regions will start to become more constrained. Use a step-by-step process to complete the grid.

PUZZLE 2

⏳ **10** MINUTES

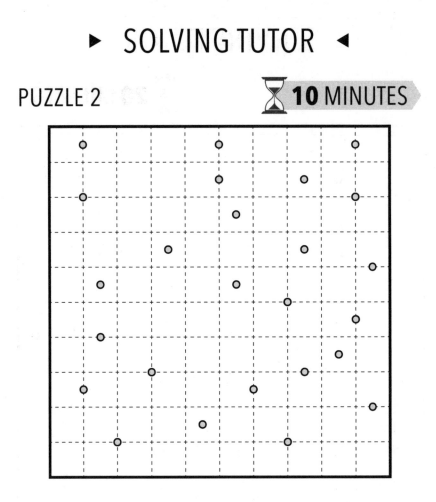

▶ Use the processes described on the previous page, but also consider which region or regions could possibly reach each particular square. For example, consider the third square in the first row. It can't connect immediately to its left, because that region is constrained by the edge of the grid, and similarly it can't be connected to the region immediately to its bottom-left for the same reason. The only options, in fact, are to connect to the second dot in the first row, or to the dot in the fourth square of the fourth row. This may not immediately help you, but as you start to solve this puzzle this and other similar deductions will be required to make progress.

PUZZLE 3

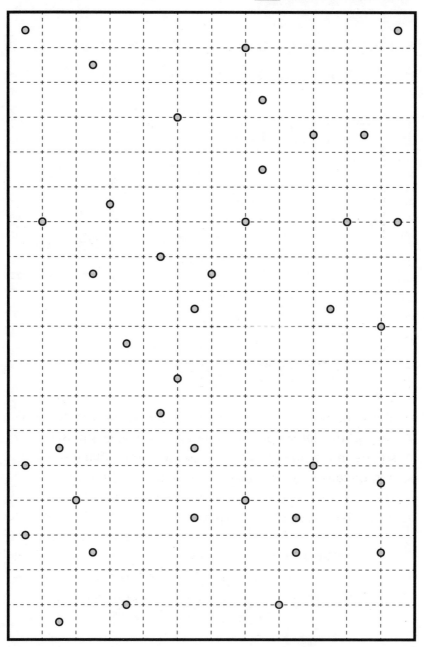

DAY
24

FUTOSHIKI

+ Place numbers so they don't repeat in rows or columns
+ All numbers must obey the inequality signs

INSTRUCTIONS

Place 1 to 4 (or whatever the width of the grid is) once each into every row and column while obeying the inequality signs. Greater than (>) signs between some cells indicate that the value in one cell is greater than that in another as indicated by the sign. The sign always points towards the smaller number.

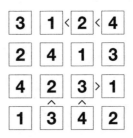

MENTAL PROCESSES

Futoshiki puzzles benefit from a clean and orderly approach, since they often have either minimal or even zero starting numbers. This means that it can be tempting to fill the grid with small pencil mark digits, but this can quickly become overwhelming. A slow and steady approach can often turn out to be faster overall than a rushed attempt.

Expert solving time
40 MINUTES

PUZZLE 1 (1–5)

▶ Start by looking at the second column. All but one of the squares is marked as being greater than another square, which means that there is only a single square which can possibly contain a '1'. Mark it in.

▶ Similarly, look at the first column. All but one of the squares are *less* than another square, which means that the only remaining square must be the '5'. Mark this in too.

▶ Remember that numbers can't repeat in a row or column, so consider the fourth square down in the first column. It is greater than both the square below and the one above, so it must be at least a '3' for this to be true.

▶ Consider the second row, where we have placed a '5' and '1' already. The last square on the row is lower than three numbers all in the fourth column, so must be a '2' (since the '1' is already placed in this row).

PUZZLE 2 (1–6)

⏳ **8 MINUTES**

▶ Futoshiki puzzles require many of the same tactics used to solve sudoku puzzles, in terms of looking for squares where only one digit will fit, or conversely places in a row or column where only one digit will fit. You'll also need to check for sets of *n* numbers that can only be found in *n* squares in a region, allowing all other options to be eliminated from those squares; and the inverse, where *n* squares only contain *n* different numbers and thus those numbers can be eliminated from the rest of the region.

▶ Some futoshiki puzzles require using a technique known as 'x-wing' by sudoku aficionados. In this logical step, you look for a pair of rows in which a candidate number can only appear at the same two columns in both rows, as shown 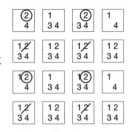 to the right by the circled '2's in rows 1 and 3. You can then eliminate that candidate from every other square in both columns, as shown by the crossed-out numbers. Or similarly vice-versa, swapping rows and columns.

▶ TRY IT ◀

PUZZLE 3 (1–7)

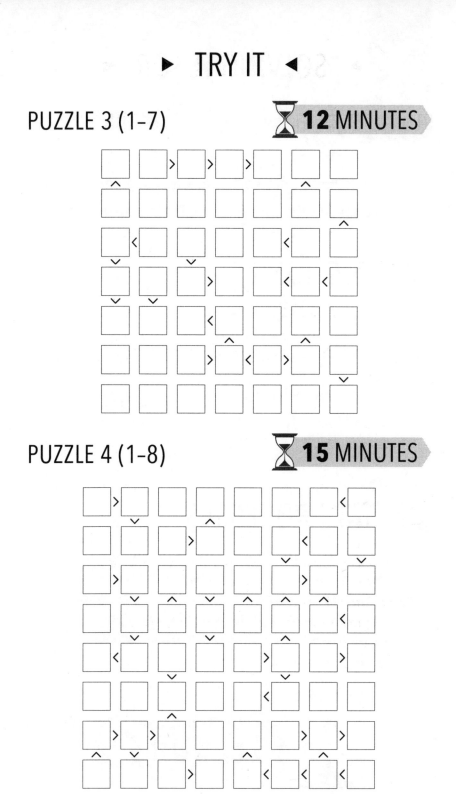

⏳ **12** MINUTES

PUZZLE 4 (1–8)

⏳ **15** MINUTES

EASY AS
A, B, C

+ Place A, B and C once each into every row and column
+ Letters outside the grid must match the nearest letter

INSTRUCTIONS

Place the given set of letters into the grid so that every row and every column contains exactly one of each letter. Usually there are more squares than letters in every row and column, so one or more squares will be empty. Letters outside the grid must match the closest letter in their row or column, as appropriate.

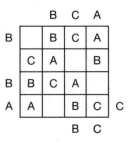

MENTAL PROCESSES

The blank squares give 'Easy As' puzzles a different feel to many other symbol-placement puzzles, and require slightly more discipline in how you make notes within the grid. Learning to pay attention to finer details, and think about negative implications as well as positives, is a useful skill.

Expert solving time
15 MINUTES

PUZZLE 1 (A, B, C)

⏳ **2 MINUTES**

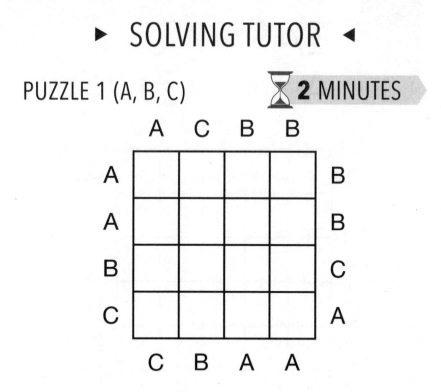

- In this puzzle, every row and column has a clue at both ends, which makes it much easier than the average 'Easy As' puzzle where this is not typically the case. It also allows you to fill in most of the squares touching an outer edge, since you can immediately place the two letters that only occur once in each row or column of clues. For example, in row 1 the A must be in column 1 and the C in column 2 because these cannot go beneath the 'B' clues.

- Next, look for rows and columns that have one of each letter already placed, and shade (or otherwise mark) the squares that must be empty so that you can easily keep track of them.

- Once you know which square is empty in a row or column, *every other square* in that row/column must have a letter in it, since there is only one empty square per row/column. Now place the outside letters from those rows/columns.

► SOLVING TUTOR ◄

PUZZLE 2 (A, B, C, D)

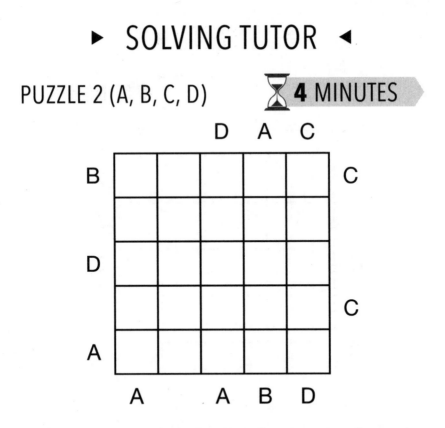

► This is an 'Easy as A, B, C, D' puzzle, where A to D must be placed in each row and column. Since it is 5×5, there is still only one blank square per row/column.

► Without every possible clue present, working out where to start is trickier. However, you have all but one clue at the bottom, so you can place B, C and D on the bottom row.

► With a C in the second square of the fifth row, the A in the bottom row is forced by the 'A' clue to the left of the grid. This in turn locates the blank square in the same row, and then both the A and D can be placed in the third column.

► Once you get stuck, use small pencil marks – or write letters spanning grid lines – to keep track of where other letters must go. This can make it easier to find further deductions.

PUZZLE 3 (A, B, C, D)   ⏳ **4** MINUTES

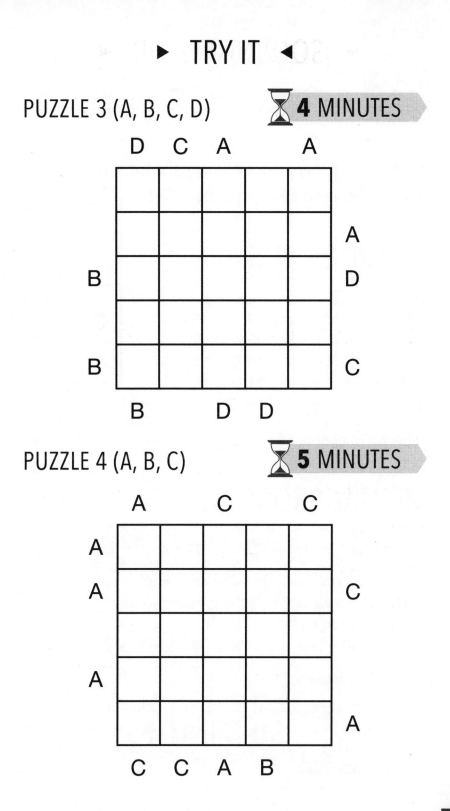

PUZZLE 4 (A, B, C)   ⏳ **5** MINUTES

TRAIN TRACKS

+ Complete a train track by linking the two entry tracks
+ Place the given numbers of track pieces

INSTRUCTIONS

Draw track pieces in some squares to complete a track that travels all the way from its entrance in the leftmost column to its exit in the bottom row. It can't otherwise exit the grid, and nor can it

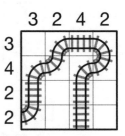

cross itself. Numbers outside the grid reveal the number of track pieces in each row and column. Every track piece must either go straight or turn a right-angle corner.

MENTAL PROCESSES

Train tracks is a similar puzzle to snake (see day 20), but without the 'no touching' constraint, and so in the same way it often rewards those solvers who are willing to take a reasoned guess at the solution. While there certainly can be step-by-step logic, it's often best to start by taking a guess at the entire solution and then trying to 'tweak' it from there.

Expert solving time
30 MINUTES

PUZZLE 1

⧗ **1** MINUTE

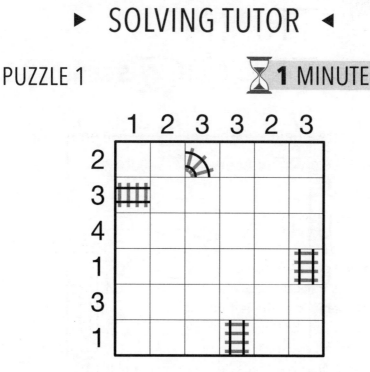

► This puzzle has two extra given pieces, in rows 1 and 4, along with the entrance and exit pieces which are always in column 1 and row 6. These make it considerably easier to solve.

► Note that row 5 can be immediately completed, since the '3' squares available must be used to link the two straight pieces in rows 4 and 6.

► Similarly, column 2 must contain two corners that connect the pieces in columns 1 and 3, completing the column.

► At this point, only one square in row 2 and four in row 3 remain to be filled in, which is relatively easily done.

► More generally, be sure to extend any given pieces into their neighbouring squares – this makes it easier to see 'at a glance' how the full train track route might fit.

PUZZLE 2

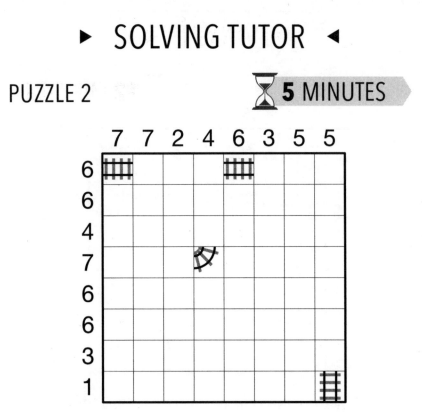

▶ The bottom row is already solved, and note also column 2 which has a '2' clue. This means that the track, once it crosses it, cannot return because that would need a total of 3 crossings (given it is already on the left of it). In turn, the two '7' clues in columns 1 and 2 must therefore be fully solved before the track reaches column 3.

▶ If you experiment, you'll see there's only one way to place '7' track pieces in both the first columns *and* connect to the given track piece in column 4 while using only '2' separate track pieces in column 3.

▶ Use similar observations to make further progress.

Note: In the final puzzle opposite, not all row and column clues are given. In the unlabelled rows and columns, any number of train segments are permitted.

PUZZLE 3

 **12** MINUTES

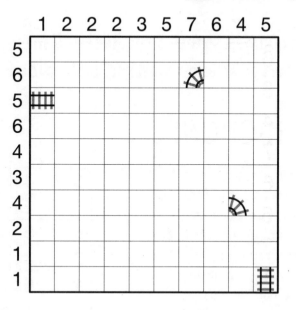

PUZZLE 4

 **12** MINUTES

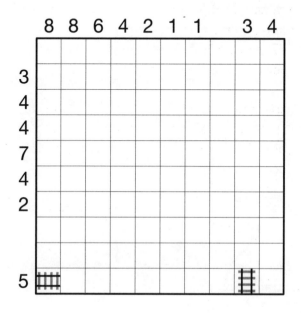

ARROW SUDOKU

+ Place numbers so they do not repeat in any region
+ Numbers on an arrow must sum to the circled number

INSTRUCTIONS

Place a number from 1 to 6 (or
whatever the width of the grid
is) into each empty square, so
that no number repeats in any
row, column or bold-lined box.
In addition, the numbers placed
along each arrow must add up to
the number in the circled square
at the start of the arrow.

3	5	4	2	6	1
1	6	2	5	3	4
6	1	5	4	2	3
2	4	3	1	5	6
4	2	6	3	1	5
5	3	1	6	4	2

MENTAL PROCESSES

Arrow sudoku requires additional types of deduction
to regular sudoku puzzles. First, it introduces simple
mathematical calculations to sudoku, but perhaps more
interestingly it adds additional thought processes to deduce
which numbers can fit with each arrow.

Expert solving time
40 MINUTES

► SOLVING TUTOR ◄

PUZZLE 1 (1-6)

⏳ **5 MINUTES**

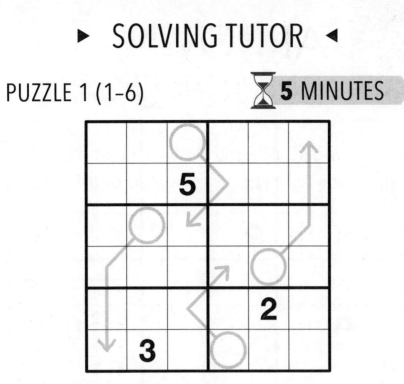

▶ The highest number to be placed in each region is a '6', so the total of each arrow must be no more than 6.

▶ Conversely, each arrow has a minimum total based on both the number of squares along it and the need to avoid repeating numbers in a region. The rightmost arrow, for example, must have a minimum (and therefore actual) value of 6, since the three squares the arrow travels along are all in the same column, so must contain 1, 2 and 3. The same applies to the leftmost arrow, for the same reason.

▶ It is generally helpful to use pencil marks (or careful observation) to keep track of which digits can fit not only along the squares along the length of each arrow but also in its circled square, since these work symbiotically together to limit which values can fit into which squares. And, of course, even when an arrow isn't fully solved it will restrict what can fit into other squares in crossing regions.

PUZZLE 2

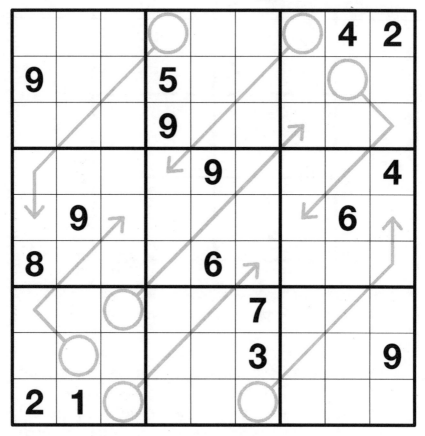

▶ If an arrow sudoku has symmetry, take advantage of this where possible to apply similar deductions to pairs of symmetric arrows. For example, in this puzzle the top-left and bottom-right arrows have similar restrictions and must each sum to 6 or more.

▶ The values along arrows, particularly long ones, are typically relatively low, so where multiple arrows cross the same region then it may heavily constrain how you can solve all of those arrows *simultaneously*.

PUZZLE 3

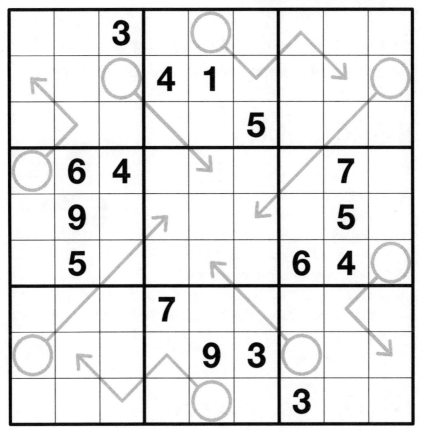

BATTLESHIPS

+ Place the given set of ships into the grid
+ Clues reveal the number of shaded squares per line

INSTRUCTIONS

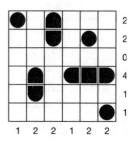

Place the given set of ships – in the
quantities and at the lengths shown
– into the grid, either horizontally or
vertically. Different ships cannot be in
touching squares – not even diagonally.
Some segments may be given, and
these may indicate a 1-square ship, the middle or the end of a
ship as appropriate. Numbers outside the grid show the exact
number of squares in their row or column that are occupied
by a ship segment.

MENTAL PROCESSES

Battleships involves a combination of straight logical
deduction, constraint satisfaction ('how can I fit *all* of these
ships simultaneously?') and sometimes organized guessing.

Expert solving time
25 MINUTES

► SOLVING TUTOR ◄

PUZZLE 1

⧖ **3** MINUTES

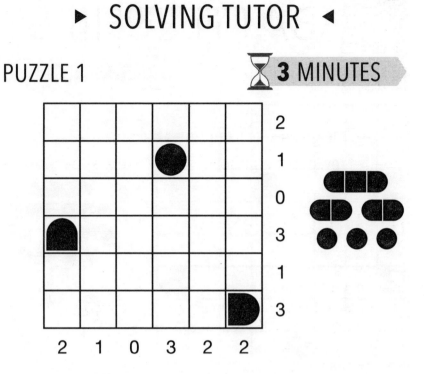

► Start by marking squares that *must* be empty, either due to a row that already has the given number of ship segments (including those with a '0' clue), or because it is touching a ship segment but can't be part of the ship itself. You could use 'x's or draw lines through them as you prefer.

► Draw in any further ship segments forced by the given segments, making sure you distinguish segments that are definitely ends from those that are yet to be decided. Cross off ships that have already been found from the list.

► Work out where the (remaining) ships can fit, and explore these options. Typically the longest ship is most restricted. In this puzzle, the 3-long ship can be placed immediately.

► Even if you aren't sure exactly where a ship goes, if you limit it to a range of squares then you may still be able to place definite 'empty' squares around central parts of it.

PUZZLE 2

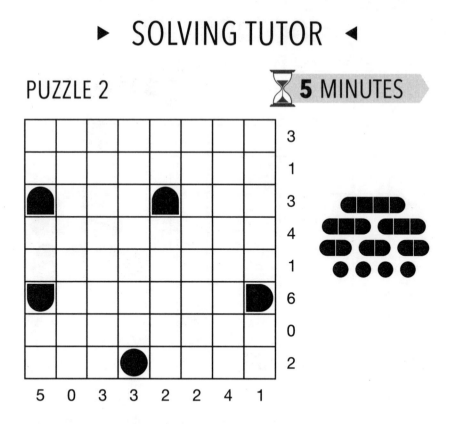

3
1
3
4
1
6
0
2

5 0 3 3 2 2 4 1

▶ This puzzle has the most common set of ships to be found in a battleship puzzle. The puzzles in this book have all clues given, but it's worth noting that there are 20 ship segments in total – so if a single clue on a side is missing, you can use basic arithmetic to restore it.

▶ Straightforward step-by-step logic, as described on the previous page, is all that's needed for the puzzle above.

▶ For puzzle 3, after some initial deductions, work out which column the 4-long ship must be in. This will allow you to be certain that the two squares in that column are occupied by it, even though you do not know exactly where it fits.

▶ In puzzle 4, keep track of the number of 2-long ships that are placed or forced and the puzzle will be straightforward.

▶ TRY IT ◀

PUZZLE 3

⏳ **8** MINUTES

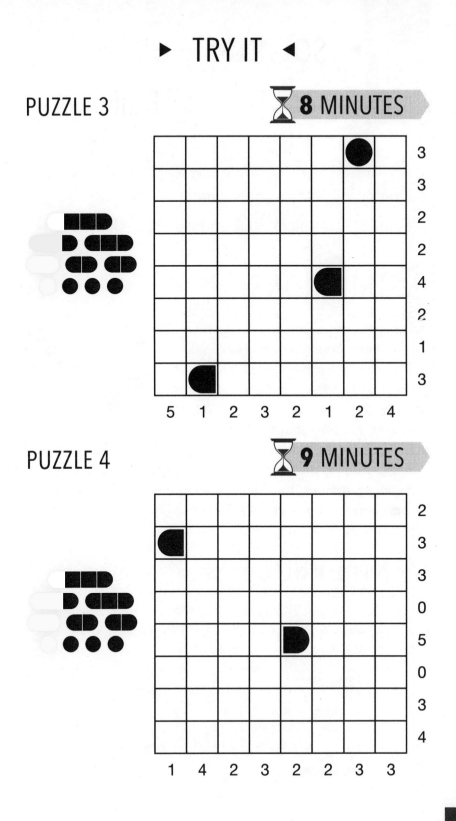

PUZZLE 4

⏳ **9** MINUTES

AKARI / LIGHT-UP

+ Place lights so that every empty square is lit
+ Lights can't shine on one another
+ Some squares block light, and may have clues in

INSTRUCTIONS

Place lights into some empty squares. Lights shine horizontally and vertically in their row and column until they meet either a black square or the edge of the grid. All squares must be lit by at least one light, but no light can shine on any other light. Some black squares contain 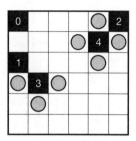 clues, specifying the exact number of touching squares (not including diagonally touching squares) which contain a light. Lights can be in any white square, not just those next to clues.

MENTAL PROCESSES

Harder puzzles require clues and/or lights to be considered in pairs (or more), leading to rewarding logical deductions.

Expert solving time
20 MINUTES

PUZZLE 1

⧗ **1 MINUTE**

▶ The '2' clue at the bottom-right is forced, since there are only two neighbouring white squares – so each of them must contain a light. Draw these in, and then draw horizontal and vertical lines from them to show which squares are already illuminated. These lines will show that the light next to the '1' in the sixth column is now forced.

▶ Mark a small 'x' in the four touching squares around the '0' clue to indicate that these can't contain a light. This in turn forces the position for the light next to the lower '1' clue.

▶ The '2' at the top left is forced by either of the lights next to the '1' clues, so draw its two lights in and trace their paths as well.

▶ There are four unlit squares in the grid, but two can't have lights in, which forces two of these squares to contain lights so that all squares are illuminated.

PUZZLE 2

⏳ **3 MINUTES**

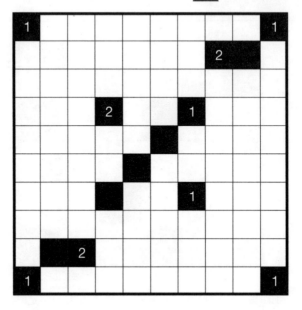

▶ Notice the '1' clues at each of the corners. Placing a light next to any one of these four clues would force the other three clues to be solved, since they all shine on each other in a loop. Picking one of these clues at random, notice that there are only two positions for a light – and no matter which position it is placed in, it results in a ring of light around the outside of the grid, as shown by these lines:

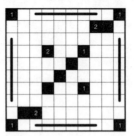

This observation allows the '2' clues in the second and penultimate rows to be solved – which then forces the exact position of the lights in the 'ring'.

► TRY IT ◄

PUZZLE 3

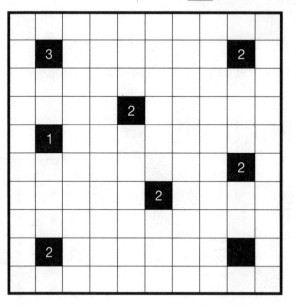

PUZZLE 4

DAY
30

KILLER SUDOKU

+ Place numbers so that they don't repeat in any region
+ Numbers in a cage must sum to the given value

INSTRUCTIONS

Place a digit from 1 to 4 (or whatever the grid size is) into each square, so that no digit repeats in any row, column, bold-lined box or dashed-line cage. The numbers in each dashed-line cage must add up to the value given at its top left.

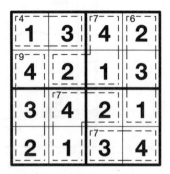

MENTAL PROCESSES

Killer sudoku requires similar thought processes to both frame sudoku and kakuro, combining as it does both simple addition with the wide range of potential sudoku reasoning techniques. It also sometimes benefits from an ability to take an overall look at the puzzle, rather than narrowly focusing on individual clues without their wider context.

Expert solving time
40 MINUTES

▶ SOLVING TUTOR ◀

PUZZLE 1 (1-6)

⏳ **10** MINUTES

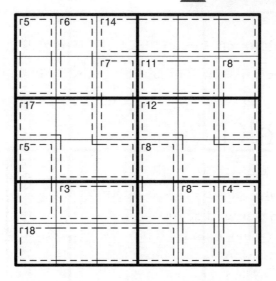

▶ Numbers can't repeat in cages, nor in the standard sudoku regions, which significantly restricts the possible values involved in each sum. For example, the '4' at the bottom right must contain 1+3, and the '18' at the bottom left must be 6+5+4+3. In fact, the restriction from the '18' allows both digits in the '4' cage to be placed.

▶ Using standard sudoku logic, there is now only one place that a '2' can fit on the bottom row of the puzzle, which in turn allows the '8' cage it is in to be solved.

▶ The bottom-right 3×2 box now only needs a '4' and '5' to be full, but the '4' can't be placed in the '8' cage and so these are both forced.

▶ Carry on making similar eliminations and deductions until the puzzle is solved.

PUZZLE 2 (1–9)

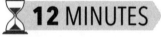
12 MINUTES

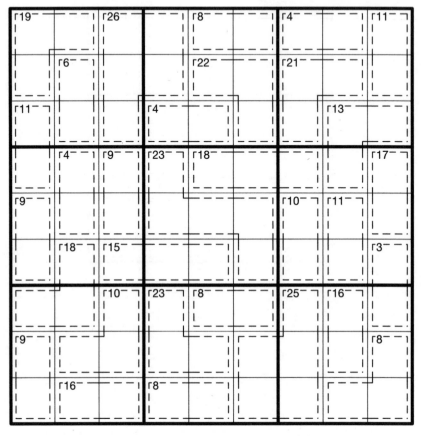

► A useful technique in killer sudoku is to look for sets of cages that almost-but-not-quite overlap with one or more sudoku regions. For example, consider the bottom-left 3×3 box. The cages in it cover that 3×3 plus one extra square. Now, you know that each 3×3 box contains digits that sum to 45 (i.e. 1+2+3+...+8+9), and similarly you can add up the four cages that cover that region and discover they sum to 53 (i.e. 18+10+9+16). The difference is 8 (i.e. 53-45), which means that the square that 'sticks out' of that region, in row 6 of column 2, must be an '8'.

PUZZLE 3 (1-9)

⏳ **18** MINUTES

STAR BATTLE

+ Place two stars into every row, column and outlined region
+ Stars can't touch – not even diagonally

INSTRUCTIONS

Place a star in certain squares, so that each row, column and bold-lined region contains exactly two stars. In addition, stars cannot touch – not even diagonally.

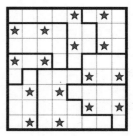

MENTAL PROCESSES

Star battle puzzles can require you to think carefully about the geographical layout of the regions on the board, and how the placement of stars in one particular location will force a cascade of other placements across the grid. They also reward you for making organized, clear notes so that you can make more complex deductions based on the results of your initial observations. Some puzzles also solve with discrete, step-by-step deductions.

Expert solving time
30 MINUTES

SOLVING TUTOR

PUZZLE 1 (1 STAR)

⏳ **2 MINUTES**

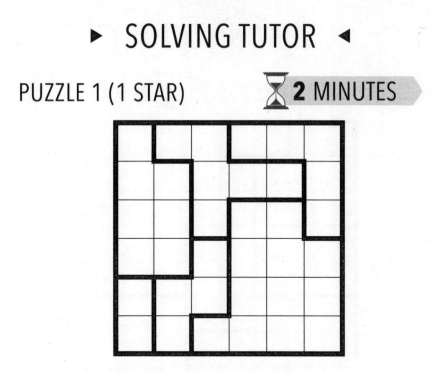

In this first puzzle, place just one star per region.

▶ The key to solving star battle puzzles is to keep track of how many stars are already accounted for in each row or column. For example, in this puzzle, there must be a star in one of the two bottom squares in the first column, thanks to the two-square region there. This then means that the rest of the column must be empty. And then this in turn forces a star in one of three squares in column 2, and then in one of two squares in column 3, and so on.

▶ Use 'x's to mark squares that must be empty, and lines to mark a range of squares where a star must be placed. For puzzles with two stars, use one or two lines as appropriate.

▶ Sometimes it helps to combine regions to make deductions. For example, the four rightmost regions are the only regions in the four rightmost columns, so must account for all of the stars in them – and so therefore could not have any stars left over to place in columns 1 or 2.

▶ SOLVING TUTOR ◀

PUZZLE 2 (2 STARS)

⧗ **8 MINUTES**

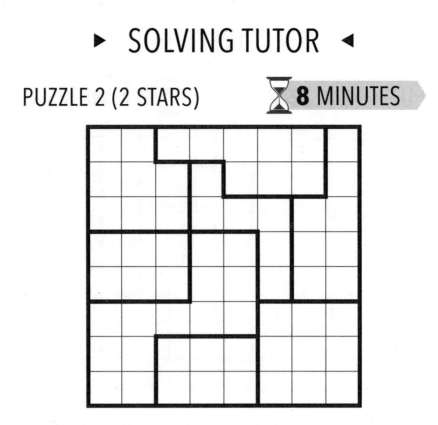

▶ Stars can't touch, even within the same region, so the two stars in both of the 3×2 regions must be in their first and third columns. In column 3 of the puzzle, all stars are now accounted for – even though you do not know their exact locations. This means you can mark several 'x's.

▶ There can't be a star in the centre of the 3×3 region, so mark an 'x'. There must of course also be four stars in the bottom two rows, which means one of these must be in the bottom two squares of column 1. Both stars in column 1 are now located, which forces the exact location of both stars in the top-left region. These in turn force the location of the two stars in the region beneath.

▶ Once you have finished the puzzle above, compare back to the example. Solutions to two-star 8×8 puzzles will always exhibit the same pattern, allowing for symmetry.

► TRY IT ◄

PUZZLE 3 (2 STARS)

⏳ **8** MINUTES

PUZZLE 4 (2 STARS)

⏳ **12** MINUTES

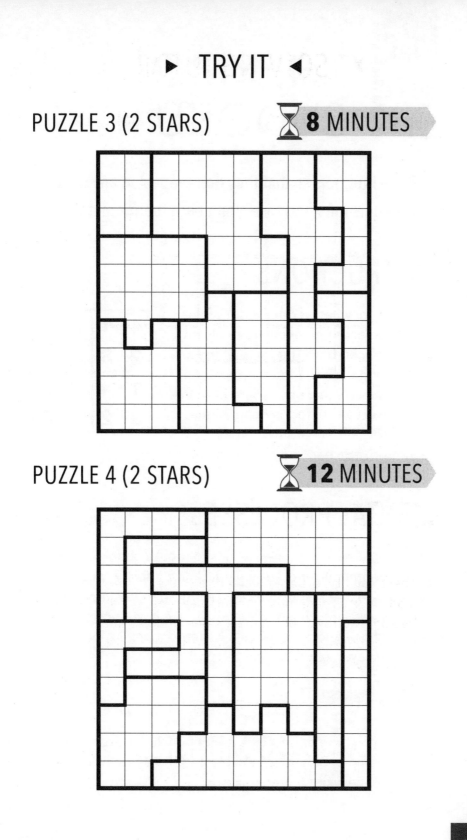

THERMO SUDOKU

+ Place numbers so that they don't repeat in any region
+ Numbers must increase along each thermometer

INSTRUCTIONS

Place 1-4 (or whatever the width of the grid) once each into every row, column and bold-lined box. The value of the digits along each shaded thermometer must increase square by square from the bulb (lowest value) to the head (highest value). This also means that digits cannot be repeated in a thermometer.

4	1	3	2
2	3	4	1
1	4	2	3
3	2	1	4

MENTAL PROCESSES

Thermo sudoku brings inequalities to regular sudoku puzzles, adding another layer of reasoning. Unlike futoshiki puzzles (see day 24), the inequalities are clearly arranged in patterns which makes it much easier to visually see how they relate to one another – and also makes it easier to more instinctively see how they might constrain the grid.

Expert solving time
40 MINUTES

► SOLVING TUTOR ◄

PUZZLE 1 (1-6)

⏳ **8 MINUTES**

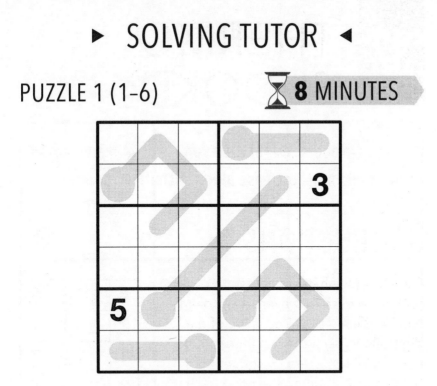

▶ A sudoku puzzle with only two given values looks like it might be tricky, but it turns out that the inequality requirements of the thermometers are very restrictive.

▶ Look at the sixth square in the fifth row, which is the third square in a four-long thermometer. It cannot be either a '3' or a '5' due to the given values, so it must be a '4'.

▶ One tactic for continuing is to use pencil mark digits, or pencil mark ranges, to keep track of which values can fit in which squares along each thermometer, as shown to the right. Now you can see, for example, that in the top-right 3×2 box the '1' must be in column 4, which forces the bottom-right thermometer to start with a '2'.

► SOLVING TUTOR ◄

PUZZLE 2 (1–9)

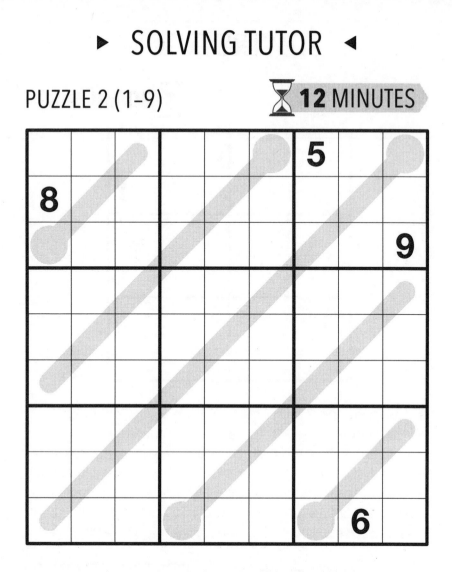

► Start by filling the long thermometer with 1–9.

► Next, the six-long thermometer on the left can be entirely filled too, thanks to the '1' in the top row and the '8' and '9' in the leftmost column.

► Look at the square in row 6 and column 7, on the six-long thermometer on the right. Due to the length of its thermometer, it cannot be lower than '4' nor higher than '7'; also, it cannot be a '5', '6' or '7' based on placed digits.

PUZZLE 3 (1–9)    **20** MINUTES

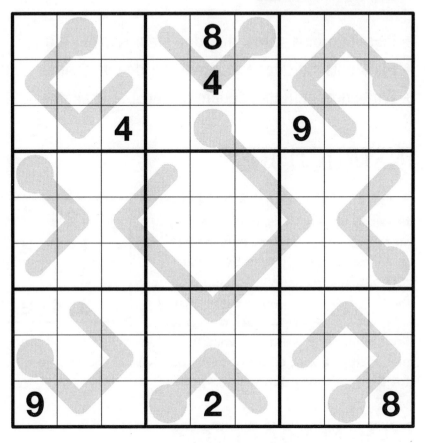

+ Place numbers so that they don't repeat in any region
+ Black dots indicates a square that is double another
+ White dots indicate a square consecutive to another

INSTRUCTIONS

Place a number from 1 to 4 (or whatever the width of the grid is) in each empty square, so no number repeats in any row or column. Squares joined by a white dot contain consecutive digits, meaning that they have a numerical difference of 1. Squares joined by a black dot contain

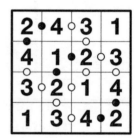

digits where one is exactly twice the value of the other. If both relationships apply, either dot may be given. **If there is no dot then neither relationship applies.**

MENTAL PROCESSES

Kropki requires careful attention to detail, with three separate types of restraint acting on all squares – and it is all too easy to forget to pay attention to the 'no dot' implications too.

Expert solving time
35 MINUTES

PUZZLE 1 (1–5)

⏳ **4 MINUTES**

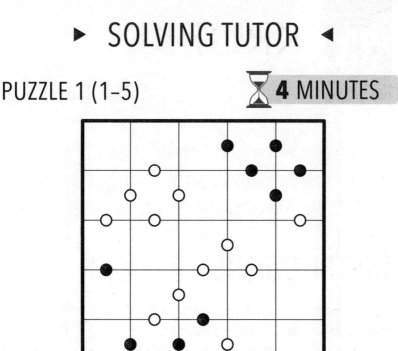

▶ There are three squares linked by two black dots on the top row. Mathematically, these must contain the sequence 4–2–1 or 1–2–4, and either way the middle square of the three is a '2'. This then in turn forces the fifth square in row 2 to also be a '2'.

▶ Two more '2's can be placed as part of the chain of three black circles at the bottom left, which leaves just a single place for a '2' to fit in the middle row.

▶ The fourth and fifth squares in the first column must contain '1' and '4' in some order. This means that the second square in the first column must contain a '3' due to the consecutive white dot, and the square above it a '5'.

▶ By elimination, '3' can now be placed in the first row – and you now know that the square to its right is *not* a '4' since there is *not* a consecutive white dot between them.

► SOLVING TUTOR ◄

PUZZLE 2 (1-6)

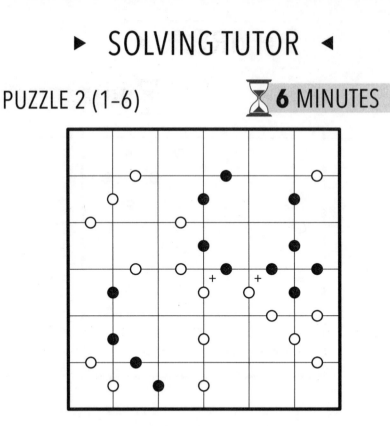

► Now the puzzle is 6×6, black dots can connect not just 1/2/4 but also 3/6. This does mean, however, that a chain of three squares linked by black dots in a single region must be 1/2/4 – but there are no such chains in this puzzle.

► Notice the two pairs of squares linked by black dots in row 3, that also connect into row 4. One must contain 1/2/4 and the other 3/6. Now look specifically at the squares labelled '+'. One must be part of the 3/6 sequence, *but* neither can be a '6' since the white dot between them would make the other a '5', which can't be in a square with a black dot attached. So one must be a '3'. But also the leftmost one can't be a '3', because if it were it would force a '2' and '4' to its left and right (in some order) thanks to the white dots – and yet we need the '2' and '4' for the other squares in the row that are linked with black dots. So the rightmost '+' square must contain a '3'.

PUZZLE 3 (1–7)

 **10** MINUTES

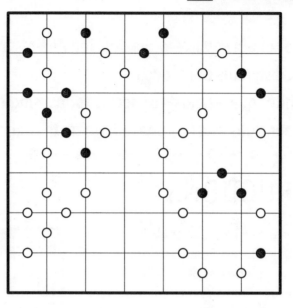

PUZZLE 4 (1–8)

15 MINUTES

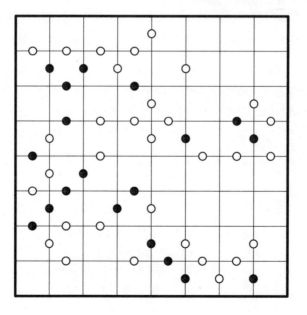

HEYAWAKE

+ Shade certain squares while obeying line-of-sight rules
+ Shaded squares can't touch
+ All white squares must connect to form a single region
+ Number clues must be obeyed, where they appear

INSTRUCTIONS

Shade certain squares so that there is never any continuous horizontal or vertical run of white squares which crosses more than one region boundary. Shaded squares cannot touch, except diagonally. All of the unshaded squares must form a single connected area,

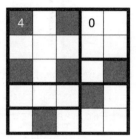

travelling left/right/up/down between squares. Numbered regions must contain exactly that many shaded squares.

MENTAL PROCESSES

Heyawake requires a mix of logical deductions and visual observation, as well as good concentration skills.

Expert solving time
15 MINUTES

► SOLVING TUTOR ◄

PUZZLE 1

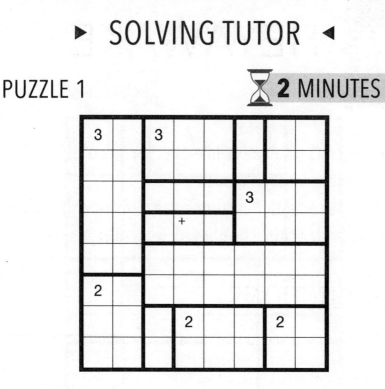

► Shaded squares can't touch, so the '2' region at the bottom right has only two options – but one of these can immediately be discounted since it would create a sealed-off white region of a single square.

► Similarly the '3' region in the 3×2 box on the top row has only two possible ways to fill it, but again one of these can be immediately ignored because it would trap a single white square against the border.

► After solving the 3×2 region in the top row, all three squares in the 3×1 region immediately beneath it must be empty, so mark these with small 'x's to keep track of this. The square marked with a '+' must now be shaded, because if it were not then there would be a continuous vertical run of unshaded squares from this square into the square two above it – but this would cross two region borders, so is not allowed.

PUZZLE 2

⏳ **5 MINUTES**

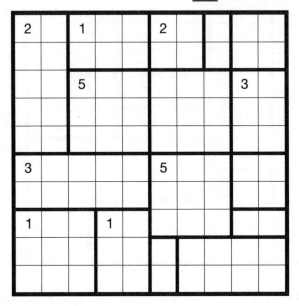

▶ The '3' region on the right-hand side of the puzzle can immediately be solved.

▶ Now consider the two '5' regions. Due to the fact that shaded squares cannot touch, there is only one way to solve each of these regions – so shade them in now.

▶ Be sure to mark 'x's in all squares around each of the solved regions, since they must either be empty in order to avoid touching a shaded square or in order to ensure that all white squares remain connected.

▶ There are various deductions that can be made at this point, but consider in particular the 2×2 '2' region on the top row. This has only two possible solutions, but notice how one of them would seal off the whole top-right area of the grid into a separate region – so can be discounted.

PUZZLE 3

8 MINUTES

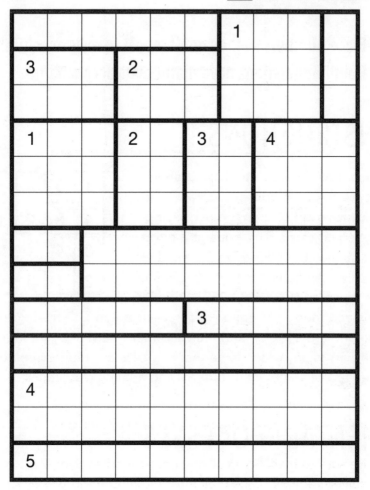

CALCUDOKU

+ Place numbers so they don't repeat in rows or columns
+ Bold-lined regions have mathematical constraints

INSTRUCTIONS

Place the numbers 1 to 4 (or whatever the width of the grid is) once each into every row and column, while obeying the region totals. The value at the top left of each bold-lined region must result when all the numbers in that region have the given operation (+, −, ×, ÷) applied

1−		96×	2−
1	2	4	3
4	3	2	1
5+ 3	2÷ 4	1	2
2	1	1− 3	4

between them. For − and ÷ operations begin with the largest number in the region and then subtract or divide by the other numbers in any order. Note that numbers *can* repeat in bold-lined regions, subject to the row and column restrictions.

MENTAL PROCESSES

Calcudoku puzzles involve a range of skills, including both mental arithmetic and sudoku-esque deduction techniques.

Expert solving time
40 MINUTES

► SOLVING TUTOR ◄

PUZZLE 1 (1–5)

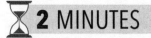 **2 MINUTES**

2–	12×	1–		
			60×	
25×	6+			
		11+	20×	3×

▶ Unlike in killer sudoku (see day 30), numbers *can* repeat in their mathematical regions, so the '11+' at the bottom left is not necessarily 1+2+3+5 as it would be in killer sudoku.

▶ The '25×' region must be equal to 5×5×1, and because numbers still *can't* repeat in a row or column, this forces the placement of all three numbers.

▶ Many other regions are heavily constrained. For example, the '20×' region must contain 4×5; the '60×' region must contain 5×4×3; the '6+' region must contain 1+2+3; and the '12×' region must contain 3×4.

▶ Combining the above observations, along with observations about not repeating a number within any row or column, the grid is now easily solved.

▶ SOLVING TUTOR ◀

PUZZLE 2 (1–6)

7+		90×		4–	
3–			7+	9+	12×
	12×				
2–	4–	5–	4÷		1–
			6×	24×	
1–					

▶ The '90×' region must be solved by 3×5×6, and the '5–' region by 6–1, which means that the fourth square in row 1 must be a '6'.

▶ With the '6' placed, the solution to the '4–' clue in row 1 must be 5–1, which in turn places the '5' from the '90×' region into row 2.

▶ With the '1', '3', '5' and '6' already in use in row 1, we can see that the '7+' region on row 1 must by process of elimination contain a '2' and '4', meaning that its remaining square (in row 2) must contain a '1'.

▶ Now consider where the '5' must be placed in column 2, given that there is already a '1' and so the '4–' must be solved by 6–2.

► TRY IT ◄

PUZZLE 3 (1–8)

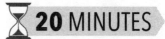 **20** MINUTES

14+		56×	18+		48×		1÷
30×							
			11+	24×		13+	
32×		16+		420×			12×
				40×			
3÷		9+			420×		
22+		64×			2−	48×	
	18×						

PUZZLE 4 (1–6)

 **10** MINUTES

In this puzzle, a '?' replaces one of the following: +, −, × or ÷.

30?			80?	9?	
	20?			3?	
		2?	18?	3?	
8?				100?	
24?		2?			16?
15?					

+ Shade squares to leave a set of unshaded islands
+ Each island must contain a number, equal to its size
+ Islands can't touch, and all shaded squares must join
+ Shaded squares can't form 2×2 areas

INSTRUCTIONS

Shade squares to leave a set of unshaded 'islands'. Each island must contain a single number, equal to the number of squares that island contains. Islands cannot touch, except diagonally. All the shaded squares must connect to form a single continuous 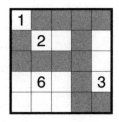 area, as in the example. In addition, no 2×2 area may be entirely shaded. Numbers cannot be added or shaded.

MENTAL PROCESSES

Nurikabe requires you to simultaneously consider several different constraints, while also being a puzzle that sometimes lends itself to inspired – and rewarding – experimentation.

Expert solving time
15 MINUTES

SOLVING TUTOR

PUZZLE 1 (1-5)

⏳ **2 MINUTES**

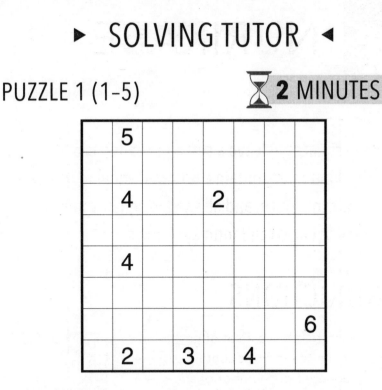

▶ Start by shading any squares directly between two numbers. This is because there can only be one number per island, and islands cannot touch. Next, see if there is any forced expansion of any islands to help them reach their target size. In this puzzle, the '3' island at the bottom must expand upwards, for example. Mark squares that are definitely empty by placing an 'x' in them.

▶ Expand all 'trapped' shaded areas until they can possibly connect, such as the squares either side of the '3'. This then forces the '3' further upwards, and completes it. Shade all around it.

▶ The '4' on the bottom row cannot expand to its right because it would then seal off the bottom-right square as a separate shaded area, so must expand upwards too.

▶ The '6' must run in a straight line upwards, since it is the only region which can reach the top-right 2×2 of the grid.

PUZZLE 2

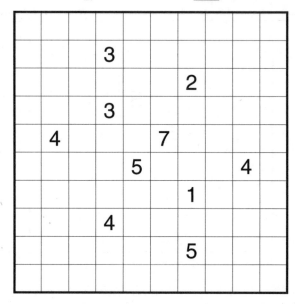

▶ Even if you don't know the exact squares used by an island, you can often at least partially expand it. In this puzzle, both the '7' and the '5' can be expanded away from the centre, since they are heavily constrained by the placement of the other numbers.

▶ Shade squares that can't be reached by any island, such as all but one of the 2×2 squares in the bottom-left corner.

▶ Every 2×2 area must contain at least one unshaded square, which often means that you know *some* squares that an island must travel to, even if you don't know exactly how it gets there. In such cases it is helpful to sketch in a rough path using lines. The bottom-left 2×2 of the grid must connect to the '4' in column 3, for example, but you don't know its exact route yet.

PUZZLE 3

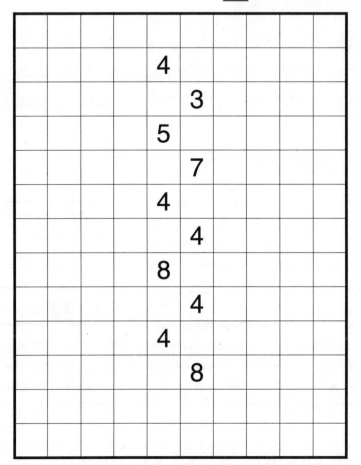

YAJILIN

+ Draw a loop that visits certain squares
+ Shade empty squares, ensuring they do not touch
+ Number clues reveal counts of some shaded squares

INSTRUCTIONS

Draw a single loop by joining empty squares with horizontal and vertical lines. Any empty squares which the loop does not visit must be shaded. Shaded squares cannot touch, except diagonally. Numbered arrows in some squares reveal how many squares in the same row or column are shaded between that arrow and the edge 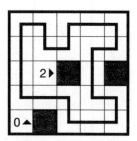 of the grid it points at. Arrow clues are not visited by the loop, and are not shaded. Not all shaded squares are necessarily identified with arrows. The loop cannot re-enter any square.

MENTAL PROCESSES

Yajilin requires you to think about the 'big picture' as you solve, since it is key to ensure the loop can always connect.

Expert solving time
18 MINUTES

PUZZLE 1

⏳ **3 MINUTES**

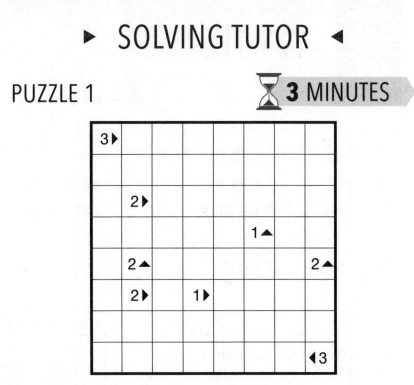

▶ The '3' clues can both be solved immediately, since for the loop to enter and exit a gap along the edge it needs at least two squares. This means the three shaded squares must be as spaced out as possible in each case.

▶ Anywhere two or more empty squares form a 'corridor' they must contain part of the loop, since shaded squares can't touch. E.g. the two squares directly beneath the top-left '3' clue must all contain parts of the path, so you can draw it in here and elsewhere:

▶ Now note how the square marked with a '+' in the part-solved picture above must be shaded, and how the square marked with a '−' must have the path pass through it due to the shaded square beneath it. From this point, the unused number clues will force the rest of the puzzle.

PUZZLE 2

⏳ **5 MINUTES**

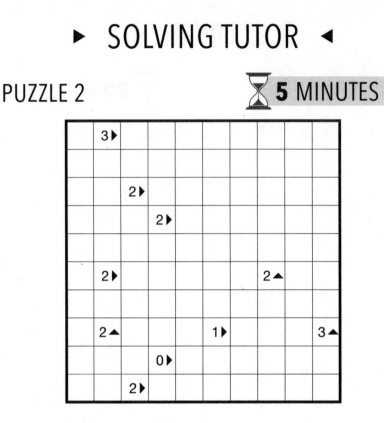

▶ As you solve, use a small 'x' to mark squares which *must* be empty so that you don't have to keep continually cross-referencing clues and other information. You can do this for all the squares pointed at by the '0' clue immediately.

▶ Note the single square trapped at the top left of the grid. The loop can't enter and exit, so it must be shaded – which in turn forces the loop to enter the square immediately beneath it, and in turn the two neighbouring squares.

▶ The bottom-left area of the grid must have the loop enter it. Also, because you cannot shade just one of the first two squares on the bottom row, you can in fact draw in the full path of the loop here immediately:

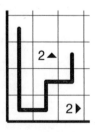

▶ TRY IT ◀

PUZZLE 3

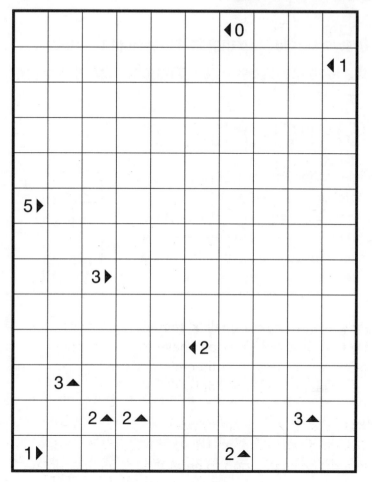

SLITHERLINK

+ Draw a single loop that joins some of the dots
+ The loop must pass by each number that many times

INSTRUCTIONS

Connect some of the dots to create a single loop, so that each digit has the specified number of adjacent line segments. Dots can only be joined by horizontal or vertical lines, and each dot can be used no more than once.

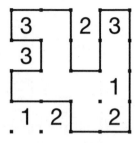

MENTAL PROCESSES

Slitherlink has simple rules that lead to many different implications, with the various interactions between clue numbers leading to a range of patterns. Requiring a mix of both local and global thinking as you solve, it rewards experimentation and encourages you to 'think outside the box' of pre-learned deductions and patterns almost every time you solve a puzzle.

Expert solving time
20 MINUTES

► SOLVING TUTOR ◄

PUZZLE 1

⏳ **2** MINUTES

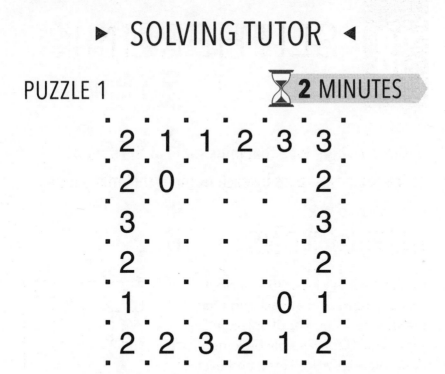

▶ When you first encounter it as a puzzle type, Slitherlink is probably best solved by experimenting, although there are a few basic observations you can use to get going.

▶ It's important to not just draw lines but also to mark 'x's between two dots that definitely *don't* connect – if you don't do so, you'll find it much harder to solve.

▶ In this puzzle, the '3' clue in the corner must have its upper and right-hand sides visited by the loop, and similarly for the '3' in row 3 column 1 since it is diagonally next to the '0'.

▶ There are now only two possibilities for the '3' clue at the top right, but one of these creates a sealed-off loop with the '3' clue immediately next to it. This forces both '3's.

▶ Extending the loop from the leftmost '3' on the top row then solves the '2' clue next to it, and step-by-step the rest of the puzzle, working anticlockwise around the edge.

▶ SOLVING TUTOR ◀

PUZZLE 2

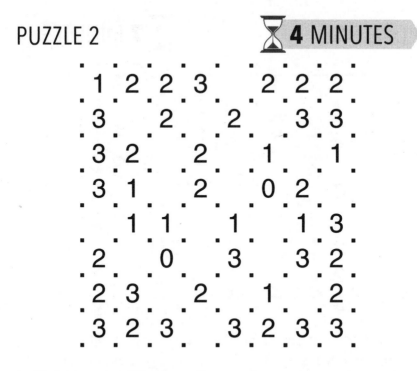

▶ Neighbouring '3's always form a zigzag pattern that runs one of two ways. In either case, parallel lines are drawn:

$$\lfloor 3 \rfloor 3 \rfloor \text{ or } \lceil 3 \lceil 3 \rceil \rightarrow \lceil 3 \mid 3 \rfloor$$

▶ A pattern is also forced for diagonally facing '3's too:

▶ A '2' in the corner of the grid, or in what is effectively a corner, forces lines either side of it: (the dotted diagonal line is useful to draw in too, to note that these points must connect directly)

▶ Chains of diagonal '2's can also force one another, as shown in the diagram to the right – so look out for how solving a '2' might cause a diagonal 'ripple' effect.

▶ TRY IT ◀

PUZZLE 3

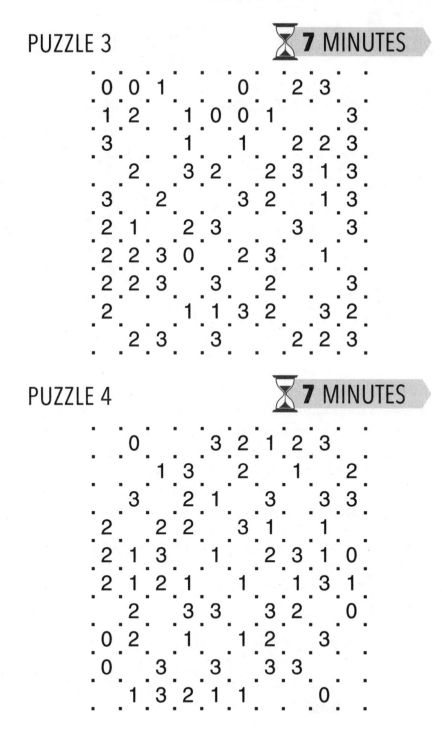

PUZZLE 4

JIGSAW SUDOKU

+ Place digits without repeats in rows, columns or shapes

INSTRUCTIONS

Place a digit from 1 to 5 (or whatever the grid width is) into each empty square, so that no digit repeats in any row, column or bold-lined jigsaw region.

1	3	4	5	2
5	1	2	3	4
4	2	5	1	3
2	5	3	4	1
3	4	1	2	5

MENTAL PROCESSES

Jigsaw sudoku is a conceptually simple twist on sudoku but the effect of replacing the regular boxes with irregular jigsaw regions is surprisingly significant. While the logical complexity may be the same, the effective solving difficulty can often go up several levels. Part of this is because without the regular boxes it becomes much easier to miss a deduction that is relatively 'obvious'; but it's also because the exact interactions between the various regions change depending on their shape, and so you need to pay far more attention to the implications of these variations. Being more organized in your solve may also help.

Expert solving time
35 MINUTES

► SOLVING TUTOR ◄

PUZZLE 1 (1–5)

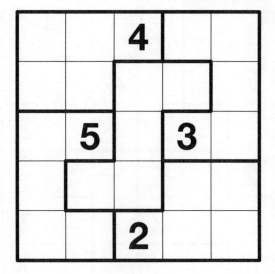

▶ The centre square is an easy start – it must be a '1', since 2, 3, 4 and 5 already appear in either its row or its column.

▶ Considering intersections between a row or column and the possible placement of a number in a jigsaw region is often the key to the puzzle. For example, the given '5' forces the '5's in rows 1 and 2 to be in the top-left and top-right jigsaw shapes – which means that there cannot be a '5' in the centre square of row 2, and then in turn the central column can be completed.

▶ The '4' on the top row forces a '4' in rows 2 or 3 of the rightmost column, which in turn means that the '4' in the bottom-right region must be in column 4. These two observations together force the placement of the '4' in the central region, and therefore the remaining '2' as well.

▶ Use similar deductions to place the remaining '2's next.

► SOLVING TUTOR ◄

PUZZLE 2 (1-6)

⏳ **10** MINUTES

► Multiple observations are often required to make progress. In this puzzle, for example, the given '1's force a '1' into each of the shaded areas shown to the right here. The lower of these two shaded areas then prevents a '1' from appearing in the two squares marked 'x'. But also the two shaded areas taken together must contain both of the '1's for columns 2 and 3, and so there also cannot be a '1' in the squares marked '+'. This forces a '1' in the square marked '-', since it is the only place it can fit in its jigsaw region.

► Now that the '1' in the bottom row is placed, a '2' can be placed on the leftmost '+'.

► More generally, you'll need to use similar multi-step logic to make further progress while solving. It's a tough puzzle.

▶ TRY IT ◀

PUZZLE 3 (1–6)

 **2** MINUTES

	3			5	
6			2		1
	1				
				1	
1		2			5
	6			4	

PUZZLE 4 (1–9)

20 MINUTES

		7			8		3	
1								
			5					7
5			8		3	6		
		6	4		9			1
3					7			
								2
	4		9			5		

SKYSCRAPERS

+ Place numbers so they don't repeat in rows or columns
+ External clues reveal the count of 'visible' numbers

INSTRUCTIONS

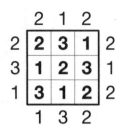

Place 1 to 3 (or whatever the width of the grid is) once each into every row and column of the grid. Place numbers in such a way that each given clue number outside the grid represents the number of digits that are 'visible' from that point, looking along that clue's row or column. A digit is always visible unless there is a higher digit preceding it, reading in order along that row or column. For example, given '231' the '2' and '3' are visible from its left, but the '1' is obscured by the higher numbers preceding it – so the clue to its left would be a '2'.

MENTAL PROCESSES

Skyscrapers requires solvers to evaluate the possible permutations of each row and column that can match with the given clues, which may have non-obvious implications.

Expert solving time
25 MINUTES

► SOLVING TUTOR ◄

PUZZLE 1 (1-4)

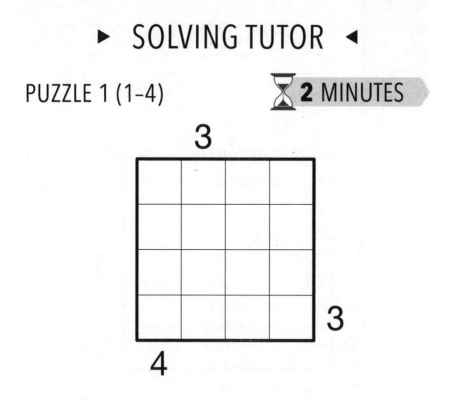

▶ Not all rows and columns are clued, which in this case helps because we have only three places to start from.

▶ The '4' clue must be solved by '1234', reading up from the bottom of the grid. In this way, none of the numbers obscure any of the other numbers, and all four are visible.

▶ To fulfil the '3' clue at the bottom right, the three remaining numbers (2, 3, 4) in the row must increase in value step by step away from the '3' clue, because the '1' at the far left can never be visible. So the bottom row is '2341', from the point of view of the '3' clue (or '1432', left to right).

▶ Now evaluate the possibilities for the remaining '3' clue. The second square down can't be a '3', so must be either a '1' or a '2'. But if it was a '2' there would be no way of fulfilling the '3' clue (since the column would need to be 1234 or 3214) – so it must be a '1', and the column '2134'.

PUZZLE 2 (1–5)

⏳ **4 MINUTES**

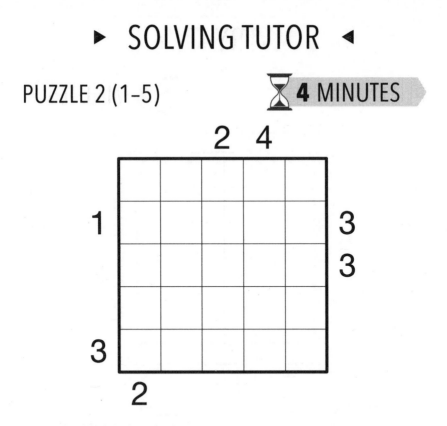

▶ The '1' clue must have a '5' directly next to it, which means that the square at the very bottom-left of the grid must contain either a '3' or a '4' in order to fulfil the '2' clue beneath it – but it can't contain a '4' due to the '3' clue next to the same square, so must contain a '3'. This then also forces the '4' to be at the very top of the first column.

▶ In row 2 of the puzzle, column 3 can't contain a '4' since if it did the '2' clue at the top of the grid would not be solvable. Similarly, row 2 column 4 can't contain a '4' due to the '4' clue at the top of the grid. And finally row 2 column 5 can't contain a '4' due to the '3' clue next to it, so the '4' in this row must be in column 2.

▶ The '4' just placed in row 2 now forces a '3' in the rightmost column of the row.

PUZZLE 3 (1–6)

⧗ **4** MINUTES

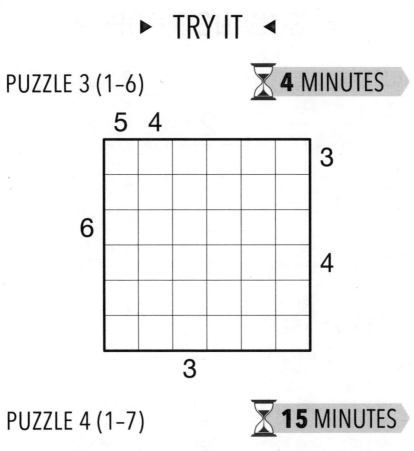

PUZZLE 4 (1–7)

⧗ **15** MINUTES

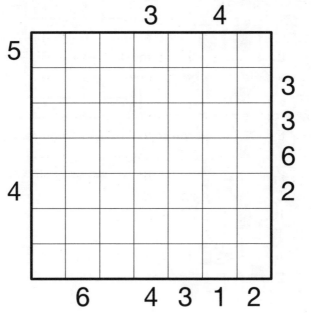

► SOLUTIONS ◄

DAY 1 PUZZLE 1

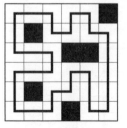

DAY 2 PUZZLE 1

4	3	3	4	0	0
1	1	4	3	4	2
1	1	2	2	2	2
3	3	1	4	1	0
0	0	2	4	3	0

DAY 1 PUZZLE 2

DAY 2 PUZZLE 2

5	5	0	2	2	4	5	5
0	2	4	4	6	4	1	0
3	3	6	3	4	6	2	1
0	4	6	3	0	1	3	5
5	2	1	2	6	3	1	1
1	2	6	0	0	4	3	6
5	6	1	0	5	4	3	2

DAY 2 PUZZLE 3

4	8	3	0	4	7	6	6	1
7	8	5	8	5	1	0	5	6
5	6	5	4	8	4	0	5	2
4	1	2	5	2	8	7	7	3
1	3	3	8	3	4	6	7	3
6	4	6	0	5	7	8	3	8
1	1	7	2	2	0	1	7	5
0	2	2	6	3	6	3	0	0
1	8	1	3	4	2	0	1	8
4	4	0	7	7	2	6	5	2

DAY 1 PUZZLE 3

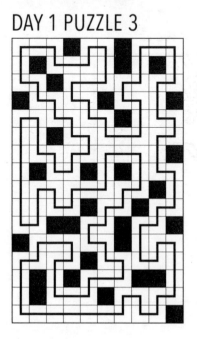

▶ SOLUTIONS ◀

DAY 3 PUZZLE 1

3	4	7	6
2	13	5	8
14	1	12	9
15	16	10	11

DAY 3 PUZZLE 2

3	2	28	26	25	24
1	4	27	29	22	23
5	7	36	19	30	21
6	8	18	35	20	31
9	11	14	17	34	32
10	13	12	15	16	33

DAY 3 PUZZLE 3

5	4	3	43	42	45	46	52
6	2	40	41	44	47	53	51
1	7	39	61	60	54	48	50
10	8	38	28	62	59	55	49
9	11	27	37	29	63	58	56
24	26	12	17	36	30	64	57
25	23	18	13	16	35	31	32
22	21	20	19	14	15	34	33

DAY 3 PUZZLE 4

85	86	87	88	89	79	78	77	99	98
84	83	82	81	80	90	76	75	97	100
53	54	55	56	91	92	74	94	1	96
52	50	48	57	45	43	93	73	95	2
51	49	47	46	58	44	42	72	3	4
65	66	67	61	60	59	71	41	7	5
64	63	62	68	69	70	40	18	8	6
33	35	36	37	38	39	19	9	17	11
34	32	29	25	24	23	20	16	10	12
31	30	28	27	26	22	21	15	14	13

DAY 4 PUZZLE 1

DAY 4 PUZZLE 2

▶ SOLUTIONS ◀

DAY 4 PUZZLE 3

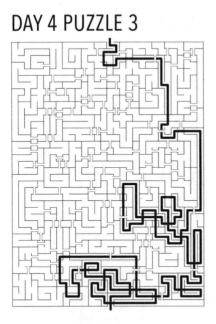

DAY 5 PUZZLE 1

2	5	1	6	4	3
4	3	6	5	2	1
6	4	2	1	3	5
5	1	3	2	6	4
3	2	5	4	1	6
1	6	4	3	5	2

DAY 5 PUZZLE 2

7	8	5	4	1	2	3	6	9
3	6	2	9	8	7	5	1	4
1	9	4	6	5	3	2	7	8
4	2	3	1	7	8	6	9	5
9	1	8	5	3	6	7	4	2
6	5	7	2	4	9	1	8	3
8	7	1	3	2	4	9	5	6
2	4	9	7	6	5	8	3	1
5	3	6	8	9	1	4	2	7

DAY 5 PUZZLE 3

9	1	7	6	8	5	2	4	3
4	3	8	1	9	2	7	5	6
5	2	6	4	7	3	9	8	1
6	9	2	3	1	4	5	7	8
7	4	1	8	5	9	6	3	2
3	8	5	2	6	7	4	1	9
8	5	3	9	4	6	1	2	7
2	7	9	5	3	1	8	6	4
1	6	4	7	2	8	3	9	5

DAY 5 PUZZLE 4

6	2	4	7	5	1	8	3	9
9	1	7	8	3	6	2	5	4
5	8	3	9	4	2	6	1	7
2	4	6	1	7	5	9	8	3
3	9	1	4	2	8	7	6	5
8	7	5	6	9	3	1	4	2
1	5	2	3	8	9	4	7	6
4	3	8	2	6	7	5	9	1
7	6	9	5	1	4	3	2	8

▶ SOLUTIONS ◀

DAY 6 PUZZLE 1

▶ $12 = 5 + 4 + 3$
▶ $22 = 5 + 14 + 3$
▶ $31 = 12 + 8 + 11$

DAY 6 PUZZLE 2

▶ $70 = 13 + 25 + 32$
▶ $82 = 36 + 38 + 8$
▶ $94 = 36 + 38 + 20$

DAY 6 PUZZLE 3

▶ $75 = 10 + 22 + 28 + 15$
▶ $112 = 27 + 18 + 35 + 32$
▶ $124 = 33 + 39 + 28 + 24$

DAY 6 PUZZLE 4

▶ $53 = 8 + 10 + 35$
▶ $79 = 21 + 34 + 24$
▶ $92 = 31 + 37 + 24$

DAY 7 PUZZLE 1

There are 45 rectangles.

DAY 7 PUZZLE 2

There are 100 rectangles.

DAY 7 PUZZLE 3

There are 441 rectangles.

DAY 7 PUZZLE 4

There are 69 rectangles.

DAY 8 PUZZLE 1

DAY 8 PUZZLE 2

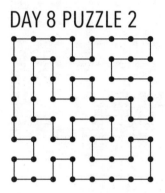

DAY 8 PUZZLE 3

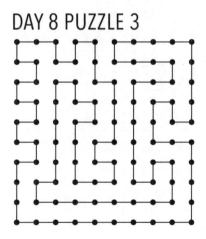

DAY 8 PUZZLE 4

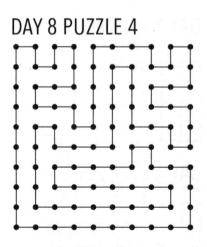

DAY 9 PUZZLE 3

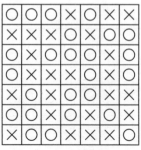

DAY 9 PUZZLE 1

DAY 9 PUZZLE 4

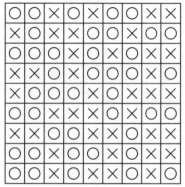

DAY 9 PUZZLE 2

DAY 10 PUZZLE 1

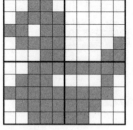

Duck

► SOLUTIONS ◄

DAY 10 PUZZLE 2

Globe

DAY 10 PUZZLE 3

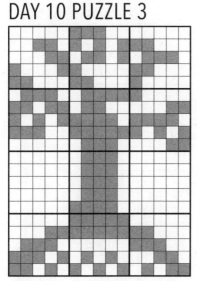

Tree

DAY 11 PUZZLE 1

5	5	5	5	5
2	2	1	2	2
4	4	5	5	1
4	2	5	2	2
4	2	5	5	1

DAY 11 PUZZLE 2

5	5	1	5	5	5	5	5
4	5	5	1	4	4	4	4
4	4	5	2	2	3	3	3
3	4	11	3	4	4	2	2
3	3	11	3	3	4	4	1
2	2	11	11	11	3	3	3
1	11	11	11	4	4	4	4
11	11	11	5	5	5	5	5

DAY 11 PUZZLE 3

12	5	5	5	5	5	7	7	8	1
12	12	12	6	6	6	6	7	8	7
12	4	12	6	7	7	7	7	8	7
4	4	12	6	8	8	8	8	8	7
5	4	12	12	12	12	7	7	7	7
5	5	5	5	12	2	2	3	3	3
6	6	6	2	2	1	4	4	4	4
6	7	6	6	1	2	2	5	5	5
7	7	7	2	2	5	5	13	5	4
8	7	8	8	8	2	5	13	5	4
8	7	8	8	8	2	5	13	4	4
8	7	8	1	8	13	5	13	5	5
8	8	12	12	12	13	1	13	5	5
8	8	8	1	12	13	13	13	13	5
12	12	12	12	12	12	12	12	13	13

▶ SOLUTIONS ◀

DAY 12 PUZZLE 1

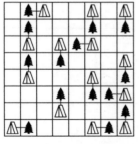

DAY 12 PUZZLE 2

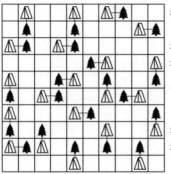

DAY 12 PUZZLE 3

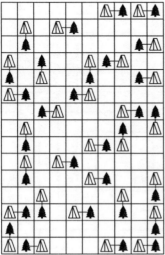

DAY 13 PUZZLE 1

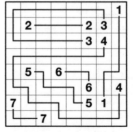

DAY 13 PUZZLE 2

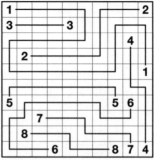

DAY 13 PUZZLE 3

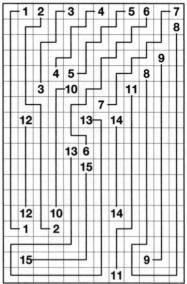

► SOLUTIONS ◄

DAY 14 PUZZLE 1

DAY 14 PUZZLE 2

DAY 14 PUZZLE 3

DAY 15 PUZZLE 1

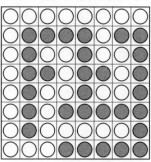

DAY 15 PUZZLE 2

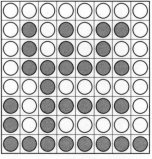

DAY 15 PUZZLE 3

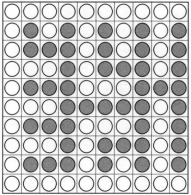

► SOLUTIONS ◄

DAY 15 PUZZLE 4

DAY 16 PUZZLE 3

4	H	A	E	B	2	D	2	A	C	F	6	7	3	1	9	1
2	8	9	1	C	H	C	5	7	9	8	9	G	E	D	E	B
6	3	6	E	9	2	1	2	A	D	F	8	B	7	1	5	8
E	8	8	D	6	7	1	A	1	B	5	B	C	4	9	3	2
3	6	3	2	E	3	7	2	9	H	F	A	B	B	1	G	4
7	8	G	3	G	F	A	H	A	9	1	9	5	C	E	4	C
4	9	4	2	1	3	5	2	6	G	F	H	B	4	C	E	A
G	D	H	7	5	1	2	8	D	4	D	F	7	9	E	B	C
F	B	A	G	A	5	9	3	3	G	H	H	D	2	8	C	6
B	G	2	7	F	G	3	C	5	6	B	E	B	H	A	1	9
5	2	6	4	7	9	H	1	B	3	G	H	E	D	A	H	H
A	D	B	6	3	1	H	F	4	F	E	C	8	6	7	D	9
9	F	E	G	4	2	4	7	B	8	7	5	6	1	A	A	H
C	8	D	A	B	1	B	1	H	G	9	4	2	E	2	E	3
5	E	5	F	D	2	8	4	C	B	H	7	9	A	A	6	1
B	8	F	C	H	C	G	2	E	2	7	D	1	5	6	8	D
D	1	7	9	C	E	A	6	C	G	2	G	3	B	5	F	7

DAY 16 PUZZLE 1

6	7	3	4	6	1	6
7	2	5	7	1	7	4
4	3	6	1	6	2	6
1	7	6	7	4	2	5
3	6	3	5	3	4	7
7	7	1	2	6	5	3
2	1	4	3	1	6	7

DAY 17 PUZZLE 1

DAY 16 PUZZLE 2

4	7	1	6	3	8	3	4
2	1	3	7	5	7	4	6
5	4	1	8	1	6	5	3
1	3	4	3	8	7	6	7
6	2	2	1	2	3	8	4
1	3	8	1	7	7	2	5
3	8	6	5	6	2	1	6
1	6	5	3	4	7	7	2

DAY 17 PUZZLE 2

► SOLUTIONS ◄

DAY 17 PUZZLE 3

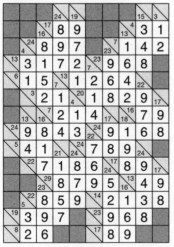

DAY 18 PUZZLE 1

F	E	D	B	A	C
B	A	F	C	D	E
C	D	B	E	F	A
E	F	C	A	B	D
A	B	E	D	C	F
D	C	A	F	E	B

DAY 18 PUZZLE 2

A	F	G	E	D	C	B
D	E	C	B	F	G	A
C	G	D	A	E	B	F
F	B	E	G	C	A	D
G	A	F	D	B	E	C
E	D	B	C	A	F	G
B	C	A	F	G	D	E

DAY 18 PUZZLE 3

B	A	C	E	G	D	F
D	G	F	A	B	C	E
C	E	D	G	F	A	B
G	F	A	B	D	E	C
A	B	E	F	C	G	D
F	C	G	D	E	B	A
E	D	B	C	A	F	G

DAY 18 PUZZLE 4

B	D	E	H	G	F	C	A
C	F	G	D	A	E	B	H
H	B	C	E	F	G	A	D
E	A	D	B	H	C	F	G
G	C	F	A	D	B	H	E
F	E	H	G	C	A	D	B
D	G	A	F	B	H	E	C
A	H	B	C	E	D	G	F

DAY 19 PUZZLE 1

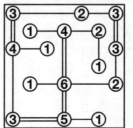

177

► SOLUTIONS ◄

DAY 19 PUZZLE 2

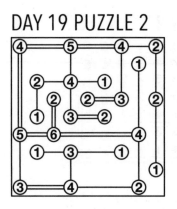

DAY 20 PUZZLE 1

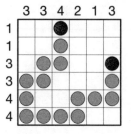

DAY 19 PUZZLE 3

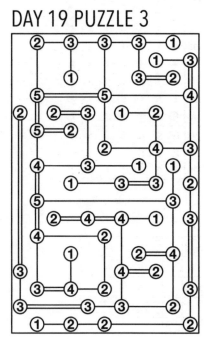

DAY 20 PUZZLE 2

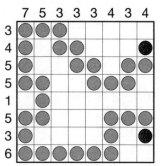

DAY 20 PUZZLE 3

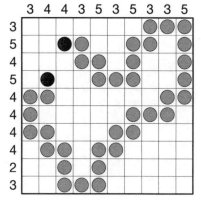

► SOLUTIONS ◄

DAY 20 PUZZLE 4

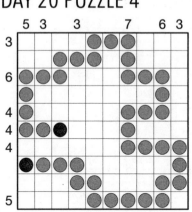

DAY 21 PUZZLE 1

	8	6	7	7	7	7	
7	2	1	4	5	6	3	14
14	6	5	3	2	1	4	7
8	3	4	1	6	5	2	13
13	5	6	2	4	3	1	8
13	4	3	6	1	2	5	8
8	1	2	5	3	4	6	13
	5	5	11	4	6	11	

DAY 21 PUZZLE 2

	11	23	11	8	18	19	17	21	7	
13	3	8	2	4	7	5	9	6	1	16
21	7	9	5	1	2	6	3	8	4	15
11	1	6	4	3	9	8	5	7	2	14
22	9	7	6	8	4	3	2	1	5	8
16	5	3	8	2	6	1	4	9	7	20
7	4	2	1	9	5	7	6	3	8	17
9	2	4	3	7	8	9	1	5	6	12
22	8	5	9	6	1	4	7	2	3	12
14	6	1	7	5	3	2	8	4	9	21
	16	10	19	18	12	15	16	11	18	

DAY 21 PUZZLE 3

	6	30	4	15	12	4	
10	2	5	1	3	6	4	72
72	3	6	4	5	2	1	10
60	5	2	6	1	4	3	12
12	1	4	3	2	5	6	60
36	6	3	2	4	1	5	20
20	4	1	5	6	3	2	36
	24	3	10	24	3	10	

DAY 21 PUZZLE 4

	96	12	315	90	42	96	10	216	168	
42	3	2	7	9	1	4	5	8	6	240
36	4	1	9	5	6	8	2	3	7	42
240	8	6	5	2	7	3	1	9	4	36
378	9	7	6	1	3	2	4	5	8	160
24	1	8	3	4	5	7	9	6	2	108
40	5	4	2	6	8	9	7	1	3	21
216	6	9	4	3	2	5	8	7	1	56
48	2	3	8	7	9	1	6	4	5	120
35	7	5	1	8	4	6	3	2	9	54
	84	135	32	168	72	30	144	56	45	

DAY 22 PUZZLE 1

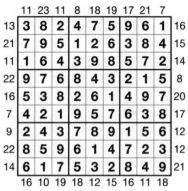

► SOLUTIONS ◄

DAY 22 PUZZLE 2

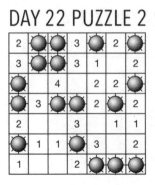

DAY 22 PUZZLE 3

DAY 22 PUZZLE 4

DAY 23 PUZZLE 1

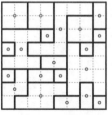

DAY 23 PUZZLE 2

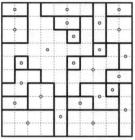

DAY 23 PUZZLE 3

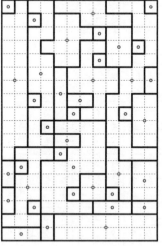

▶ SOLUTIONS ◀

DAY 24 PUZZLE 1

```
4  2  1  5  3
5  1  4  3  2
1  3  2  4  5
3  4  5  2  1
2  5  3  1  4
```

DAY 24 PUZZLE 2

```
3  2  6  5  1  4
6  4  5  1  2  3
5  3  1  4  6  2
1  5  2  3  4  6
2  1  4  6  3  5
4  6  3  2  5  1
```

DAY 24 PUZZLE 3

```
6  7  5  3  2  1  4
7  2  1  6  5  4  3
3  4  6  2  1  7  5
2  6  4  1  3  5  7
1  5  3  4  7  2  6
4  1  7  5  6  3  2
5  3  2  7  4  6  1
```

DAY 24 PUZZLE 4

```
8  7  2  3  6  1  4  5
3  1  7  5  2  4  8  6
7  6  5  8  4  2  1  3
1  5  8  6  7  3  2  4
2  3  6  4  8  7  5  1
4  8  1  2  5  6  3  7
5  4  3  7  1  8  6  2
6  2  4  1  3  5  7  8
```

DAY 25 PUZZLE 1

```
      A   C   B   B
 A  | A | C | B |   | B
 A  |   | A | C | B | B
 B  | B |   | A | C | C
 C  | C | B |   | A | A
      C   B   A   A
```

DAY 25 PUZZLE 2

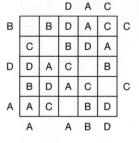

```
           D   A   C
 B  |   | B | D | A | C | C
    | C |   | B | D | A |
 D  | D | A | C |   | B |
    | B | D | A | C |   | C
 A  | A | C |   | B | D |
      A       A   B   D
```

▶ SOLUTIONS ◀

DAY 25 PUZZLE 3

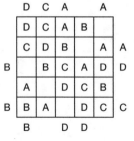

DAY 25 PUZZLE 4

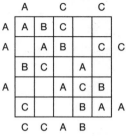

DAY 26 PUZZLE 1

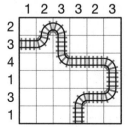

DAY 26 PUZZLE 2

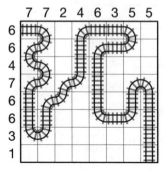

DAY 26 PUZZLE 3

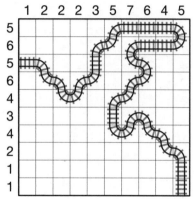

DAY 26 PUZZLE 4

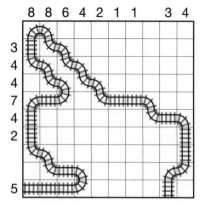

► SOLUTIONS ◄

DAY 27 PUZZLE 1

4	2	③	6	5	1
6	1	5	2	4	3
5	⑥	1	4	3	2
3	4	2	①	⑥	5
1	5	4	3	2	6
2	3	6	⑤	1	4

DAY 27 PUZZLE 2

5	6	3	⑧	7	1	⑨	4	2
9	4	1	5	3	2	6	⑧	7
7	2	8	9	4	6	1	5	3
1	7	6	3	9	5	8	2	4
4	9	2	7	1	8	3	6	5
8	3	5	2	6	4	7	9	1
3	5	⑨	6	2	7	4	1	8
6	⑧	4	1	5	3	2	7	9
2	1	⑦	4	8	⑨	5	3	6

DAY 27 PUZZLE 3

1	4	3	9	⑦	8	2	6	5
6	7	⑤	4	1	2	9	③	⑧
9	2	8	3	6	5	7	1	4
⑧	6	4	5	2	9	1	7	3
3	9	7	1	4	6	8	5	2
2	5	1	8	3	7	6	4	⑨
4	3	9	7	8	1	5	2	6
⑤	1	6	2	9	3	④	8	7
7	8	2	6	⑤	4	3	9	1

DAY 28 PUZZLE 1

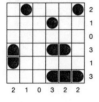

DAY 28 PUZZLE 2

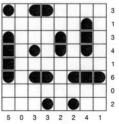

DAY 28 PUZZLE 3

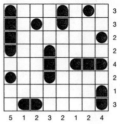

DAY 28 PUZZLE 4

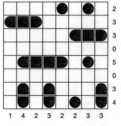

DAY 29 PUZZLE 1

► SOLUTIONS ◄

DAY 29 PUZZLE 2

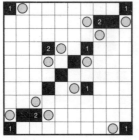

DAY 30 PUZZLE 1

2	5	6	1	3	4
3	1	4	6	5	2
5	4	3	2	1	6
1	6	2	3	4	5
4	2	1	5	6	3
6	3	5	4	2	1

DAY 29 PUZZLE 3

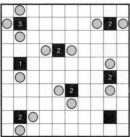

DAY 30 PUZZLE 2

9	7	8	4	2	6	1	3	5
3	2	1	7	5	9	4	8	6
5	4	6	3	1	8	9	2	7
6	3	5	1	9	7	2	4	8
2	1	4	6	8	3	7	5	9
7	8	9	2	4	5	3	6	1
4	6	3	8	7	1	5	9	2
1	5	2	9	6	4	8	7	3
8	9	7	5	3	2	6	1	4

DAY 29 PUZZLE 4

DAY 30 PUZZLE 3

2	7	5	8	3	9	6	1	4
3	4	8	6	2	1	5	7	9
9	6	1	7	4	5	2	8	3
1	9	2	4	7	3	8	5	6
6	3	7	9	5	8	1	4	2
5	8	4	1	6	2	3	9	7
7	5	9	3	1	6	4	2	8
8	2	3	5	9	4	7	6	1
4	1	6	2	8	7	9	3	5

► SOLUTIONS ◄

DAY 31 PUZZLE 1

DAY 31 PUZZLE 2

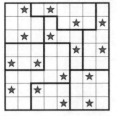

DAY 31 PUZZLE 3

DAY 31 PUZZLE 4

DAY 32 PUZZLE 1

6	4	3	1	2	5
2	1	5	4	6	3
3	6	2	5	4	1
1	5	4	6	3	2
5	3	6	2	1	4
4	2	1	3	5	6

DAY 32 PUZZLE 2

3	7	6	8	9	2	5	4	1
8	4	9	5	3	1	7	2	6
1	5	2	4	6	7	3	8	9
2	1	5	3	7	4	6	9	8
4	6	8	2	5	9	1	7	3
7	9	3	6	1	8	4	5	2
6	2	7	9	4	3	8	1	5
5	8	1	7	2	6	9	3	4
9	3	4	1	8	5	2	6	7

DAY 32 PUZZLE 3

6	2	9	5	8	3	1	4	7
3	1	8	7	4	9	6	5	2
7	5	4	2	1	6	9	8	3
1	6	3	8	7	2	4	9	5
8	4	7	1	9	5	3	2	6
5	9	2	6	3	4	8	7	1
4	7	1	3	5	8	2	6	9
2	8	5	9	6	1	7	3	4
9	3	6	4	2	7	5	1	8

DAY 33 PUZZLE 1

5	3	1	2	4
3	4	5	1	2
2	5	3	4	1
4	1	2	5	3
1	2	4	3	5

▶ SOLUTIONS ◀

DAY 33 PUZZLE 2

6	4	1	3	5	2
4	5	3	6	2	1
5	1	4	2	6	3
1	2	5	4	3	6
3	6	2	1	4	5
2	3	6	5	1	4

DAY 33 PUZZLE 3

4	3	6	2	1	7	5
2	1	5	4	7	6	3
1	2	3	7	5	4	6
3	4	2	5	6	1	7
5	6	7	3	4	2	1
6	7	4	1	3	5	2
7	5	1	6	2	3	4

DAY 33 PUZZLE 4

7	5	1	4	3	8	6	2
8	4	2	3	5	6	1	7
5	2	8	6	7	1	4	3
2	1	7	5	6	3	8	4
4	3	6	1	8	2	7	5
3	6	4	2	1	7	5	8
6	7	3	8	4	5	2	1
1	8	5	7	2	4	3	6

DAY 34 PUZZLE 1

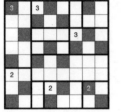

DAY 34 PUZZLE 2

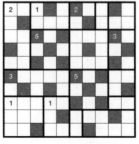

DAY 34 PUZZLE 3

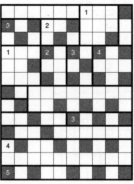

DAY 35 PUZZLE 1

2- 4	12× 3	1- 5	1	2
2	4	1	60× 3	5
25× 5	6+ 1	3	2	4
1	5	11+ 2	20× 4	3× 3
3	2	4	5	1

DAY 35 PUZZLE 2

7+ 2	4	90× 3	6	4- 5	1
3- 4	1	5	7+ 2	9+ 3	12× 6
1	12× 3	4	5	6	2
2- 3	4- 2	5- 6	4÷ 4	1	1- 5
5	6	1	6× 3	24× 2	4
1- 6	5	2	1	4	3

DAY 35 PUZZLE 3

14+ 5	4	56× 7	18+ 3	1	48× 6	8	1÷ 2
30× 3	5	8	6	7	1	2	4
2	1	5	11+ 4	24× 3	8	13+ 7	6
32× 4	8	16+ 3	7	420× 6	2	5	12× 1
1	6	2	5	40× 8	7	4	3
3÷ 6	2	9+ 1	8	5	420× 4	3	7
22+ 8	7	64× 4	1	2	3	2- 6	48× 5
7	18× 3	6	2	4	5	1	8

DAY 35 PUZZLE 4

30? 1	2	5	80? 4	9? 6	3
3	20? 1	4	5	3? 2	6
4	5	2? 2	18? 6	3? 3	1
8? 2	6	1	3	100? 4	5
24? 6	4	2? 3	1	5	16? 2
15? 5	3	6	2	1	4

DAY 36 PUZZLE 1

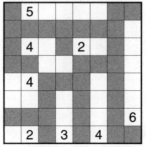

DAY 36 PUZZLE 2

DAY 36 PUZZLE 3

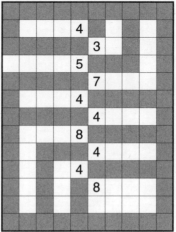

▶ SOLUTIONS ◀

DAY 37 PUZZLE 1

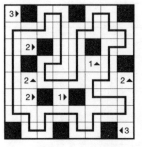

DAY 37 PUZZLE 2

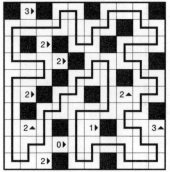

DAY 37 PUZZLE 3

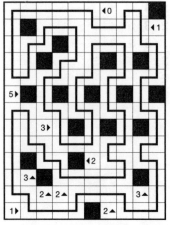

DAY 38 PUZZLE 1

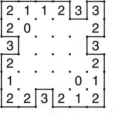

DAY 38 PUZZLE 2

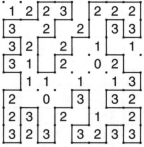

DAY 38 PUZZLE 3

◆ SOLUTIONS ◆

DAY 38 PUZZLE 4

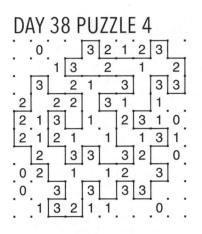

DAY 39 PUZZLE 4

4	6	7	1	5	8	2	3	9
1	7	9	3	6	5	4	2	8
6	8	3	5	2	4	9	1	7
5	9	2	8	1	3	6	7	4
7	5	4	2	3	1	8	9	6
2	3	6	4	8	9	7	5	1
3	2	8	6	9	7	1	4	5
9	1	5	7	4	6	3	8	2
8	4	1	9	7	2	5	6	3

DAY 39 PUZZLE 1

3	2	4	5	1
5	1	3	2	4
4	5	1	3	2
2	4	5	1	3
1	3	2	4	5

DAY 39 PUZZLE 2

1	5	3	2	4	6
6	3	1	4	2	5
4	6	5	3	1	2
2	1	6	5	3	4
3	4	2	6	5	1
5	2	4	1	6	3

DAY 39 PUZZLE 3

2	3	1	6	5	4
6	5	4	2	3	1
4	1	3	5	2	6
5	2	6	4	1	3
1	4	2	3	6	5
3	6	5	1	4	2

DAY 40 PUZZLE 1

3

4	2	1	3
3	1	2	4
2	3	4	1
1	4	3	2

3

4

DAY 40 PUZZLE 2

2 4

	4	2	3	1	5	
1	5	4	1	2	3	3
	2	3	5	4	1	3
	1	5	2	3	4	
3	3	1	4	5	2	

2

► SOLUTIONS ◄

DAY 40 PUZZLE 3

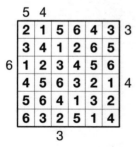

DAY 40 PUZZLE 4

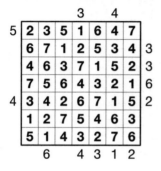

MEMORY
C⊗ACH

TRAIN AND SUSTAIN A
MEGA-MEMORY IN
40 DAYS

DR GARETH MOORE

Enjoyed this book? Then try a companion volume from the same author: *Memory Coach*. It includes a complete programme of exercises, techniques and tips that will help you ensure your memory never lets you down again.

With exercises that target specific issues, as well as general-purpose memory workouts, the book is packed with information and strategies for use in everyday life, while also providing a guided plan for progression that continues to build upon the techniques you have already covered on previous days. Along with the exercises themselves, you'll find plenty of information on what the exercises are actually doing for you and why they are important in maintaining memory function.

Available in all good bookshops. ISBN: 978-1-78929-018-9.

Enjoyed this book? Then try a companion volume from the same author: *Brain Coach*. It includes a complete programme of exercises, techniques and tips that will help you overcome mental strain, increase your brain function and train your brain.

Containing exercises and tests that target specific issues, as well as general puzzles that will make sure your brain gets an 'all brain' workout every day, you will learn how to optimize the performance of your brain, how 'downtime' for your brain can enhance your mental powers, how to spark your creativity, improve your vocabulary for clearer thinking, deal with unhelpful brain responses – and much more besides.

Available in all good bookshops. ISBN: 978-1-78929-019-6.